Nuffield Primary Science
SCIENCE PROCESSES AND CONCEPT EXPLORATION

Living processes

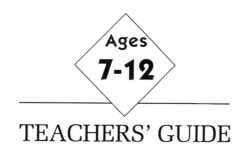

Ages
7-12

TEACHERS' GUIDE

PUBLISHED FOR THE NUFFIELD–CHELSEA CURRICULUM TRUST BY COLLINS EDUCATIONAL

NUFFIELD PRIMARY SCIENCE
Science Processes and Concept Exploration

Directors
Paul Black
Wynne Harlen

Deputy Director
Terry Russell

Project members
Robert Austin
Derek Bell
Adrian Hughes
Ken Longden
John Meadows
Linda McGuigan
Jonathan Osborne
Pamela Wadsworth
Dorothy Watt

First published 1993 by Collins Educational
An imprint of HarperCollins*Publishers*
77-85 Fulham Palace Road
London W6 8JB

Second edition published 1995

Copyright © Nuffield-Chelsea Curriculum Trust 1993, 1995

ISBN 0 00 310257 2

Printed and bound by Scotprint Ltd, Musselburgh

Design by Carla Turchini, Chi Leung
Illustrations by John Booth, Gay Galsworthy,
Maureen Hallahan, Mary Lonsdale, Sally Neave,
Karen Tushingham
Cover artwork by Karen Tushingham

Photograph acknowledgements
Page 28: Natural History Photographic Agency
Page 38: John Birdsall
Page 54: Timothy Woodcock
Page 78: Frank Lane Picture Agency

Commissioned photography by Oliver Hatch

The Trust and the Publishers would like to thank the
governors, staff and pupils of Hillbrook Primary School,
Tooting, for their kind co-operation with many of the
photographs in this book.

Safety adviser
Peter Borrows

Other contributors
Elizabeth Harris
Carol Joyes
Anne de Normanville
Ralph Hancock

Trial schools

The SPACE Project and the Trust are grateful to the
governors, staff, and pupils of all the trial schools. It will
be obvious to readers of these guides how much we are
indebted to them for their help, and especially for the
children's drawn and written records of their hard work
and their growing understanding of science.

All Saints Primary School, Barnet, Hertfordshire
Ansdell County Primary School, Lytham St Anne's,
Lancashire
Bishop Endowed Church of England Junior School,
Blackpool
Brindle Gregson Lane Primary School, Lancashire
Brookside Junior and Infants School, Knowsley
Chalgrove JMI School, Finchley, London N3
Christ the King Roman Catholic Primary School, Blackpool
English Martyrs Roman Catholic Primary School,
Knowsley
Fairlie County Primary School, Skelmersdale, Lancashire
Fairway JMI School, Mill Hill, London NW7
Foulds Primary School, Barnet, Hertfordshire
Frenchwood County Primary School, Preston
Grange Park Primary School, London N21
Hallesville Primary School, Newham, London E6
Heathmore Primary School, Roehampton, London SW15
Honeywell Junior School, London SW11
Huyton Church of England Junior School, Knowsley
Longton Junior School, Preston
Mawdesley Church of England Primary School, Lancashire
Moor Park Infants School, Blackpool
Mosscroft County Primary School, Knowsley
Nightingale Primary School, London E18
Oakhill Primary School, Woodford Green, Essex
Park Brow County Primary School, Knowsley
Park View Junior School, Knowsley
Purford Green Junior School, Harlow, Essex
Ronald Ross Primary School, London SW19
Rosh Pinah School, Edgeware, Middlesex
Sacred Heart Junior School, Battersea, London SW11
St Aloysius Roman Catholic Infants School, Knowlsey
St Andrew's Roman Catholic Primary School, Knowsley
St Bernadette's Roman Catholic Primary School, Blackpool
St James's Church of England Junior School, Forest Gate,
London E7
St John Fisher Roman Catholic Primary School, Knowsley
St John Vianney Roman Catholic Primary School,
Blackpool
St Mary and St Benedict Roman Catholic Primary School,
Bamber Bridge, Preston
St Peter and St Paul Roman Catholic Primary School,
Knowsley
St Theresa's Roman Catholic Primary School, Blackpool
St Theresa's Roman Catholic Primary School, Finchley,
London N3
Scarisbrick County Primary School, Lancashire
Selwyn Junior School, London E4
Snaresbrook Primary School, Wanstead, London E18
South Grove Primary School, Walthamstow, London E17
Southmead Infants School, London SW19
Staining Church of England Primary School, Blackpool
Walton-le-Dale County Primary School, Preston
West Vale County Primary School, Kirkby
Woodridge Primary School, North Finchley, London N12

Contents

Explanation of symbols in the margins

 Warning

 Good opportunities to develop and assess work related to Experimental and Investigative Science

 Notes which may be useful to the teacher

 Vocabulary work

 Opportunities for children to use information technology

 Equipment needed

 Reference to the pupils' books

CHAPTER 1

Introduction

1.1 The SPACE approach to teaching and learning science

A primary class where the SPACE approach to science is being used may not at first seem different from any other class engaged in science activities; in either, children will be mentally and physically involved in exploring objects and events in the world around them. However, a closer look will reveal that both the children's activities and the teacher's role differ from those found in other approaches. The children are not following instructions given by others; they are not solving a problem set them by someone else. They are deeply involved in work which is based on their own ideas, and they have taken part in deciding how to do it.

The teacher has, of course, prepared carefully to reach the point where children try out their ideas. She or he will have started on the topic by giving children opportunities to explore from their own experience situations which embody important scientific ideas. The teacher will have ensured that the children have expressed their ideas about what they are exploring, using one or more of a range of approaches – from whole class discussion to talking with individual children, or asking children to write or draw – and will have explored the children's reasons for having those ideas.

With this information the teacher will have decided how to help the children to develop or revise their ideas. That may involve getting the children to use the ideas to make a prediction, then testing it by seeing if it works in practice; or the children may gather further evidence to discuss and think about. In particular, the teacher will note how 'scientific' children have been in their gathering and use of evidence; and should, by careful questioning, encourage greater rigour in the use of scientific process skills.

It is essential that the children change their ideas only as a result of what they find themselves, not by merely accepting ideas which they are told are better.

By carefully exploring children's ideas, taking them seriously and choosing appropriate ways of helping the children to test them, the teacher can move children towards ideas which apply more widely and fit the evidence better – those which are, in short, more scientific.

You will find more information about the SPACE approach in the Nuffield Primary Science *Science Co-ordinators' handbook.*

1.2 Useful strategies

Finding out children's ideas

This guide points out many opportunities for finding out children's ideas. One way is simply by talking, but there are many others. We have found the following strategies effective. How you use them may depend on the area of science you are dealing with. In Chapter 3 you will find examples of these strategies. More information about them is given in the *Science Co-ordinators' handbook*.

Talking and open questioning

Whole class discussions can be useful for sharing ideas, but they do not always give all children a chance to speak. It is often helpful if children are allowed to think of their own ideas first, perhaps working them out in drawings, and are then encouraged to share these with others – perhaps with just one other child, or with a larger group.

Annotated drawings

Asking children to draw their ideas can give a particularly clear insight into what they think. It also gives you a chance to discuss the children's ideas with them. Words conveying these ideas can then be added to the drawing, either by you or by the child. Such work can be kept as a permanent record.

Sorting and classifying

This can be a useful way of helping children to clarify their ideas and to record their thinking. They could sort a collection of objects or pictures into groups.

Writing down ideas

Children may instead write down their responses to questions you pose. Writing gives children the opportunity to express their own views, which can then be shared with others or investigated further.

Log books and diaries

These can be used to record changes over a longer investigation. They need not necessarily be kept by individual children, but could be kept by a whole group or class. Children can jot down their ideas, as words or drawings, when they notice changes, recording their reasons for what they observe.

Helping children to develop their ideas

Letting children test their own ideas

This will involve children in using some or all of the process skills of science:

- observing
- measuring
- hypothesizing
- predicting
- planning and carrying out fair tests
- interpreting results and findings
- communicating

It is an important strategy which can, and should, be used often. The *use* of process skills *develops* them – for example, through greater attention to detail in observing, more careful control of variables in fair tests, and taking all the evidence into account in interpreting the results.

Encouraging generalization from one context to another

Does an explanation proposed for a particular event fit one which is not exactly the same, but which involves the same scientific concept? You or the children might suggest other contexts that might be tried. This might be done by discussing the evidence for and against the explanation, or by gathering more evidence and testing the idea in the other context, depending on children's familiarity with the events being examined.

Discussing the words children use to describe their ideas

Children can be asked to be quite specific about the meaning of words they use, whether scientific or not. They can be prompted to think of alternative words which have almost the same meaning. They can discuss, where appropriate, words which have special meaning in a scientific context, and so be helped to realize the difference between the 'everyday' use of some words and the scientific one.

Extending the range of evidence

Some of the children's ideas may be consistent with the evidence at present available to them, but could be challenged by extending the range of evidence. This applies particularly to things which are not easily observed, such as slow changes; or those which are normally hidden, such as the insides of objects. Attempts to make these imperceptible things perceptible, often by using secondary sources, help children to consider a wider range of evidence.

Getting children to communicate their ideas

Expressing ideas in any way – through writing, drawing, modelling or, particularly, through discussion – involves thinking them through, and often rethinking and revising them. Discussion has a further advantage in that it is two-way and children can set others' ideas against their own. Just realizing that there are different ideas helps them to reconsider their own.

1.3 Equal opportunities

The SPACE approach to teaching and learning science gives opportunities for every child to build on and develop his or her experiences, skills and ideas. It can therefore be used to benefit pupils of all kinds and at any stage of development. This is fully discussed in the *Science Co-ordinators' handbook*.

1.4 Living processes and the curriculum

This teachers' guide is divided into four themes; in each one there is a section on finding out children's ideas, examples of ideas children have, and a section on helping children to develop their ideas.

Nuffield Primary Science Themes

How do we know if it is alive?

This theme indicates ways in which children might be helped to develop their ideas about what is living and non-living.

Young children may have little concept of what is alive; some may only associate movement or human features with living things. Children's experience of the processes common to all living things may be limited, consequently they may have little difficulty in fully appreciating that all living things have common processes such as feeding, breathing, growth and reproduction.

Within this theme, children can explore their local environment for living and non-living things. Through sorting and classifying activities, children's criteria for recognizing living things may be challenged, and children may be brought nearer to a more scientific understanding of what is alive.

Keeping healthy

This theme indicates ways in which children might be helped to develop their ideas about living more healthy lives.

Many children associate keeping healthy more with diet than with exercise. Those who consider exercise to be important often suggest adult activities rather than children's active pastimes. In general, children know that particular foods may be healthy to eat but they may not be fully aware of what is needed to make up a healthy diet.

Within this theme ways are suggested in which children can consider their own diet and exercise. They can find out about the types of food needed in a balanced diet, and the benefits of regular exercise to their breathing and circulatory systems. They can become more aware of the harmful substances encountered in everyday life, the long-term effects of smoking, and the use and abuse of drugs.

In some of the activities, children record their daily routines, interview adults, search secondary sources and devise ways of promoting healthy living. Some activities from the theme 'The human body' may also be helpful in further developing children's ideas encountered here.

The human body

This theme indicates ways in which children might be helped to develop their ideas about the human body, growth and reproduction.

Although children may know of particular organs in the human body, many appear to be unaware of the functions of these organs and the organ system of which they form part. Some children think that food remains whole inside the body; others may think that air enters the body and is expelled unchanged. Children may be unaware that blood circulates. The role of parents in reproduction may not be understood.

Within this theme ways are suggested in which children can come to a better understanding of the digestive, breathing and circulatory systems in the body, and of human growth and reproduction. Activities are presented in which children investigate their breathing and pulse rates, and relate these to body processes. They can examine X-ray photographs and bones, and observe their own movements to come to an understanding of the different muscle systems, bones and joints in the human body. Although ways are suggested for helping children to develop their ideas about reproduction, work on this should be in accordance with the school's policy on sex education.

National Curriculum Programmes of Study	Environmental Studies 5-14 (Scotland): Science
Life Processes and Living Things **1 Life processes** **a** that there are life processes, including nutrition, movement, growth and reproduction, common to animals, including humans; **b** that there are life processes, including growth, nutrition and reproduction, common to plants.	**Understanding Living Things and the Processes of Life (Stages P4 to P6)** **Variety and characteristic features** • recognising and naming the distinguishing features of the different groups using simple keys.
Life Processes and Living Things **2 Humans as organisms** **b** that food is needed for activity and for growth, and that an adequate and varied diet is needed to keep healthy; **c** a simple model of the structure of the heart and how it acts as a pump; **e** the effect of exercise and rest on pulse rate; **h** that tobacco, alcohol and other drugs can have harmful effects.	**Understanding Living Things and the Processes of Life (Stages P4 to P6)** **The processes of life** • the structure and functions of the major parts of the body as they relate to the processes of movement and nutrition.
Life Processes and Living Things **2 Humans as organisms** **c** a simple model of the structure of the heart and how it acts as a pump; **d** how blood circulates in the body through arteries and veins; **e** the effect of exercise and rest on pulse rate; **f** that humans have skeletons and muscles to support their bodies and to help them to move; **g** the main stages of the human life cycle.	**Understanding Living Things and the Processes of Life (Stages P4 to P6)** **The processes of life** • the structure and functions of the major parts of the body as they relate to the processes of movement and nutrition.

Plants

This theme indicates ways in which children might be helped to develop their ideas about plants.

Many children think that a plant is either a house plant or a herbaceous flowering plant, and do not consider such things as trees or grass to be plants. Children may not be aware that plants need food and air, and may suggest that plants only need soil, sunlight and water.

Within this theme, activities are suggested in which children can examine the structure of a flowering plant, and investigate the conditions for the germination and growth of plants. These activities may help children to become more aware of the parts of a flowering plant, the function of these parts, and the stages of reproduction in flowering plants. Children may also become more aware of the basic processes common to all living things.

1.5 Experimental and Investigative Science

Two important aspects of children's learning in science are:
◆ learning how to investigate the world around them;
◆ learning to make sense of the world around them using scientific ideas.

These are reflected in the National Curriculum. 'Experimental and Investigative Science' covers the first aspect. The second aspect is covered by the rest of the Programme of Study. Although these two aspects of science learning are separated in the National Curriculum they cannot be separated in practice. Through investigation children explore their ideas and/or test out the ideas which arise from discussion. As a result, ideas may be advanced, but this will depend on the children's investigation skills. Thus it is important to develop these skills in the context of activities which extend ideas.

You will find investigations which provide opportunities to develop investigative skills, marked in the text by the symbol shown here. In this teachers' guide, the investigations which cover the most skills are 'What keeps us healthy?' (page 46) and 'Plant growth' (page 86).

Pupils can develop their ability to do Experimental and Investigative Science, as follows:

1 'Planning experimental work'. Children should be helped to make progress from asking general and vague questions, to suggesting ideas which could be tested. Teachers' discussion with pupils should aim to help them to make predictions, using their existing understanding, on the basis of which they can decide what evidence should be collected and then children should be helped to think about what features they are going to change, what effects of these changes they are going to observe or measure, and what features they must keep the same. In this way they can come to understand what is meant by 'a fair test'.

Life Processes and Living Things

1 Life processes
b that there are life processes, including growth, nutrition and reproduction, common to plants.

3 Green plants as organisms
a that plant growth is affected by the availability of light and water; and by temperature;
b that plants need light to produce food for growth;
c that the root anchors the plant, and that water and nutrients are taken in through the root and transported to other parts of the plant;
d about the life cycle of flowering plants, including pollination, seed production, seed dispersal and germination.

Understanding Living Things and the Processes of Life (Stages P4 to P6)

The processes of life
• the structure and function of the parts of flowering plants and factors which affect germination and growth.

2 'Obtaining evidence'. Children should make observations in the light of their ideas about what they are looking for and why. When they describe their observations, teachers may have to help them to improve, for example by reminding them of their original aims and plan for the work. They should encourage progress from qualitative comparisons and judgements to making quantitative measurements. This should lead to the development of skills with a variety of instruments and to increasing care and accuracy in measurement.

3 'Considering evidence'. Children should learn to record their evidence in systematic and clear ways, starting with simple drawings and then learning to use tables, bar charts and line graphs to display the patterns in numerical data. They should be asked to think about and discuss their results, considering what might be learnt from any trends or patterns. As ideas develop, they should be careful in checking their evidence against the original idea underlying the investigation and should become increasingly critical in discussing alternative explanations which might fit their evidence. They should be helped to relate their arguments to their developing scientific understanding. They should also be guided to see possibilities for conducting their investigation more carefully, or in quite different ways.

Children's work might not follow this particular sequence of stages. For example, some might start with evidence from their observations and proceed on this basis to propose a hypothesis and a plan to test it. Useful learning about how to investigate might arise when only one or two of the above aspects of an investigation are involved, or when the teacher tells children about some aspects so that they can concentrate on others. However, there should be some occasions for all pupils when they carry out the whole process of investigation by themselves.

The assessment examples given in chapter 4 are analysed in relation to the level descriptions, which describe children's progress in relation to these three aspects of Attainment Target 1. The three aspects provide a framework both for guiding children and for assessing their progress.

CHAPTER 2

Planning

2.1 Introduction: planning with children's ideas in mind

The key scientific ideas presented in this guide can be explored in various contexts, and many of the suggested activities can be incorporated into cross-curricular topic work. This chapter uses a worked example as an aid to planning a topic. Further information on planning is given in the *Science Co-ordinators' handbook*.

A teacher using the SPACE approach should take into account:

◆ the need to find out children's own ideas, not only at the beginning of the work but also at intervals during it;
◆ the importance of planning the investigations with the children, using their ideas as the starting point;
◆ the concepts that are being explored;
◆ the direction in which the children's ideas are developing.

2.2 Cross-curricular topics

Activities which explore the ideas covered in this teachers' guide to *Living processes* may be approached via a number of topics in addition to the one set out as an example in the planning sheets (pages 15–16). It is assumed that teachers will adapt the topic to whatever local resources are of interest and readily to hand. Some possibilities are given below.

Growth

Children could look at both plant and animal life cycles, following complete cycles for vertebrates such as frogs, insects such as butterflies, locusts, and stick insects, and plants such as beans and cress. (Avoid kidney beans – they are poisonous.)
The conditions needed for plant growth might be investigated.
Measurement of plant growth, plant/tree height, tree girth, examination of annual rings.
A wild life area might be established in a small flower bed, an old bath or an area out of the school grounds.

Sex education in accordance with school policy could be included in this topic, starting with children's own growth, measurement of weight and height over time. Children could look for evidence to show how they have grown. This could lead to a consideration of the development into an adult.

Some links with other Nuffield Primary Science teachers' guides and pupils' books include:

Earth in Space – seasonal growth;

Living things in their environment – habitat study;
The variety of life – individual variation;
Rocks, soil and weather – soils and growth.

Healthy living

The topic of healthy living could be developed through a consideration of diet, exercise and rest, leisure activities and medical care.
Children could find out about their own diets by recording what they eat, investigating food labelling, and talking to those involved in food preparation.
Why do we need a balanced diet? How can we plan for a balanced diet? What types of food should be sold at a tuck shop? Children could run a tuck shop for a week.
They could design posters to inform of good diet and healthy living.
Children can compile a record of their weekly exercise and leisure activities. How long do we exercise, rest and sleep?
What sports do children engage in? What muscles do we use? What are muscles for? How do we lift and throw things?
Finding out about medical care at school and in the community could lead to children thinking about hospitals, medical centres, and health workers. Children could interview those concerned with health care.
What medicines do we take? How are drugs used to help us? How do we keep ourselves safe from abuse of drugs, alcohol, smoking? The reasons for vaccination and immunization.
Safety on the road, warnings, and protective clothing.
Health education could also be incorporated into this topic.

Some links with other Nuffield Primary Science teachers' guides and pupils' books include:

Forces and movement – carrying children and other things; human movement;
Living things in their environment – processes of decay;
Light – reflective surfaces, warning signs;
Sound and music – alarms and signals.

Food

In this topic children could look at the different types of food we eat, what happens to food in the body, how food plays a part on special occasions, and how food is prepared, grown and sold.
Children could look at their own diet, special diets, diets of vegetarians, vegans, fruitarians.
The types of food we need for a balanced diet.
The digestive system, blood flow in the body. Do we drink more in warm weather? Why? Find out about how our diet changes as we grow.
Cooking food, fuels we use in cooking. How do we keep food hot/cold? Hygiene in food preparation.
Food we have at celebrations – how is it prepared?
Where does our food come from? Types of farming, growing crops, soils, drainage. Growing plants from seeds. What conditions do plants grow in? Foods from other countries. How is food transported?
Foods eaten by animals. Caring for animals and pets.
Additives in food, colours of food, using our senses to choose and taste food. Food preservation and packaging.
Designing a package, food advertising, designing a poster.
Places we buy food.
Costing a meal.

Some links with other Nuffield Primary Science teachers' guides and pupils' books include:

The variety of life – different food plants;
Using energy – types of fuel;
Electricity and magnetism – kitchen appliances;
The Earth in Space – seasonal growth;
Rocks, soil and weather – growth in different types of soil.

Ourselves

In this topic children can find out about the organ systems in their bodies, their means of support and movement, as well as how we can keep healthy.
They can acquire the knowledge which will inform some of the choices they make about food, exercise, and ways of keeping safe.
Some children could find out about their family history, as well as talking about hobbies and interests.
Children can investigate the ways in which their neighbourhood has developed.
The plan on page 15 shows how 'Ourselves' could be developed through a cross-curricular approach.

Some links with other Nuffield Primary Science teachers' guides and pupils' books include:

The variety of life – comparing people;
Materials – clothing and protection;
Living things in their environment – human needs.

2.3 Topic plan examples

The plans on pages 15 and 16 illustrate how the science related to *Living processes* may be embedded in a cross-curricular topic. The topic presented is 'Ourselves' and opportunities for exploring mathematics, language, history, geography, design technology and art have been indicated on the first plan. On the second plan the science work has been amplified to illustrate possible areas of exploration based within the overall topic. It is important to remember these are only examples and are not intended to be exhaustive.

2.4 Use of information technology

Specific examples of opportunities to use information technology are indicated by this symbol in the margin and referred to in the text. The examples include:

- word processing to produce reports of investigations
- simple databases to record and analyse data collected about children in the class, such as breathing rates
- 'decision trees' devised by the children for the classification of groups of objects.

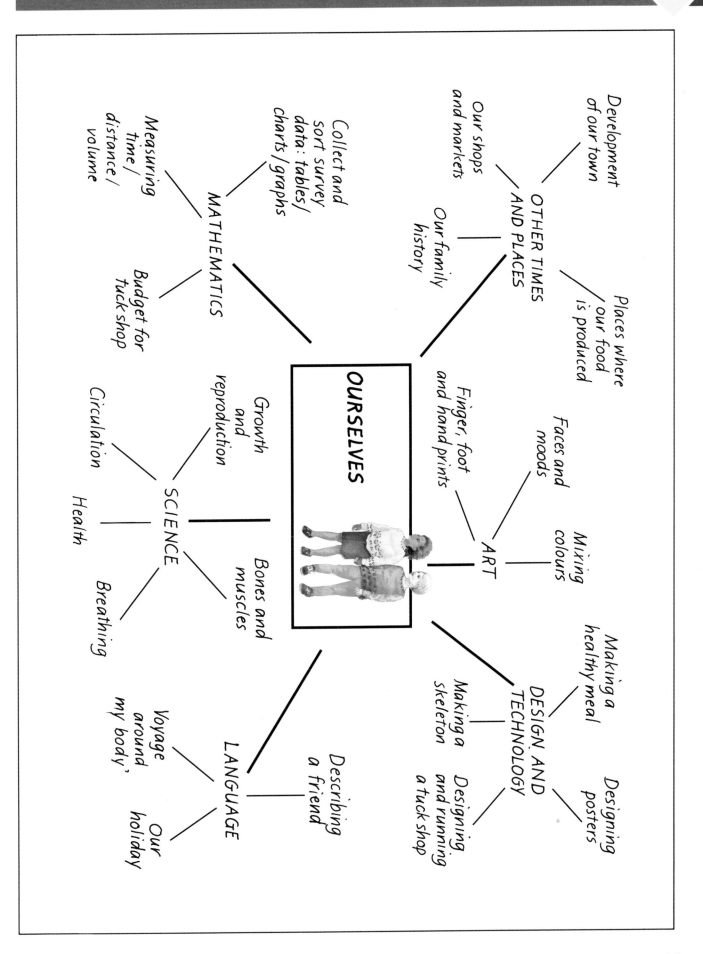

OURSELVES

OTHER TIMES AND PLACES
- Development of our town
- Places where our food is produced
- Our shops and markets
- Our family history

MATHEMATICS
- Collect and sort survey data: tables / charts / graphs
- Measuring time / distance / volume
- Budget for tuck shop

SCIENCE
- Growth and reproduction
- Circulation
- Health
- Breathing
- Bones and muscles

ART
- Faces and moods
- Finger, foot and hand prints
- Mixing colours

DESIGN AND TECHNOLOGY
- Making a healthy meal
- Making a skeleton
- Designing and running a tuck shop
- Designing posters

LANGUAGE
- Describing a friend
- 'Voyage around my body'
- Our holiday

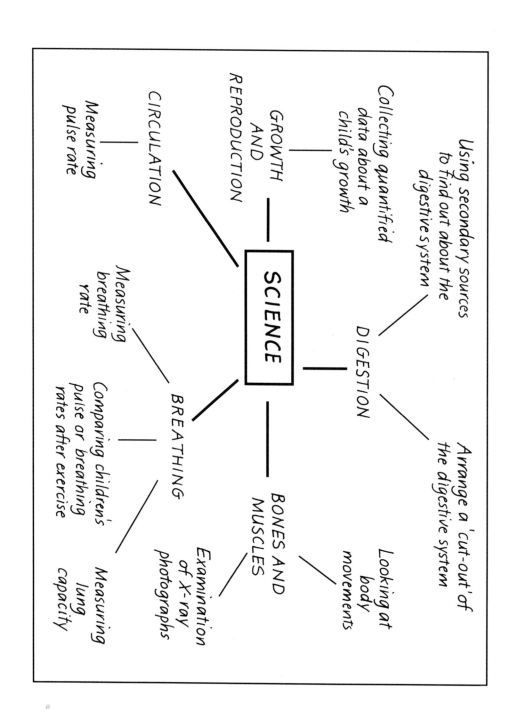

2.5 Pupils' books

The pupils' books accompanying this guide are called *Living Things in Action* for the lower juniors and *More About Living Things in Action* for the upper juniors. The pupil books are intended to be used spread by spread. The spreads are not sequential, and they are covered in these notes in thematic order.

Features of the pupil books include:

◆ Stimulus spreads, often visual, designed to raise questions, arouse curiosity, and to promote discussion.

◆ Information spreads, which give secondary source material in a clear and attractive way.

◆ Activity ideas, to form the basis of investigations to be carried out by the children.

◆ Cross-curricular spreads and stories which can act as a basis for creative writing, or spreads with a historical or creative focus.

◆ Real life examples of applications of science in the everyday world.

Living things in action

You are what you eat pages 4–5

Purpose: To help children develop the idea that the kind of food they eat is important; to act as a language spread, in which a variety of forms are used.

Ideas for discussion: The answers to the question about the saying are: 'An apple a day...' yes – to remain healthy, we are advised to eat at least five portions of fruit and vegetables a day. 'Brown sugar is better...' is not true. 'Carrots help you see in the dark' – is true in that they contain beta carotene. The body can turn this into vitamin A, a deficiency of which can cause 'night blindness'. 'Spinach makes you strong...' is true, in that green vegetables contain vitamins and minerals which are essential for a healthy body.

Pupils' books cross-references: Energy, pages 6-7.

Teachers' guide cross-references: Living processes, pages 13, 40, 44, 51-2.

What's in a burger? pages 6–7

Purpose: To help children think about the origins of food, using the example of a familiar meal.

Extension activity: Get children to draw their own burger pictures and to use arrows and boxes to explain the sources of all the different components.

Pupils' books cross-references: Materials, pages 20-1.

Teachers' guide cross-references: Living processes, pages 13, 15.

Plants as food pages 22–23

Purpose: To help children to develop the idea of food and its natural origins; to look at the range of plants, and the various parts of them, that we eat.

Extension activities: Encourage children to look in their own bathrooms for products inspired by natural products. Do they contain real plant extracts? Assemble a display in the classroom of herbs, spices and bathroom products.

What's up Doc? pages 16–17

Purpose: To build on children's own experiences; to introduce the idea of weakness of the body, and keeping healthy.
Note: This work may require some intervention from the teacher, and discussion, to help the children recount their own experiences.
Extension activity: Invite the school nurse into the classroom so that the children can ask him or her questions.

What happens when you eat? pages 2–3

Purpose: To inform children about digestion.
Extension activity: Children could devise a dance routine based on the processes in digestion.
Teachers' guide cross-references: Living processes, pages 13, 15, 67–9.

Them bones pages 8–9

Purpose: To provide material for reference and discussion.
Notes: All mammals have seven neck bones. The skeletons are a lizard (top) and a rabbit (below). The astronaut has been putting much less strain on his or her bones than would be the case on Earth. This causes calcium from the bones to be lost into blood. The bones become smaller, and the astronaut shrinks.
Extension activity: Encourage the children to feel and identify their own bones.
Teachers' guide cross-references: Living processes, pages 14, 57, 63-4, 73-5.

Muscles and movement pages 10–11

Purpose: To provide material for reading for information about movement and muscles.
Extension activity: Discuss the questions on page 11, and get children to feel their joints and bend them.
Teachers' guide cross-references: Living processes, pages 14, 73.

The senses pages 12–13

Purpose: To give children a simple introduction to the five main senses.
Pupils' books cross-references: Light, pages 10-11; More about sound and music pages, 6-7, 8-9; Time and Space, pages 18-19.
Teachers' guide cross-references: Living processes, page 14; Light, pages 46–48; Materials, page 56; Sound and music, pages 43–7.

More sense pages 14–15

Purpose: To help children to compare animal and human senses.
Note: The poetry provides a link with English.
Pupils' book cross-references: Sound pages 8-9.
Teachers' guide cross-references: Light, page 48; Sound and music, page 43.

Animals wild and tame pages 18–19

Purpose: A simple classifying activity.
Notes: The cow is related to the bison, the dog to the wolf and the pig to the boar. Camels only exist in the wild if they are feral (that is, they or their ancestors were once domesticated but now live in the wild). The African elephant (shown here) is related to the Indian elephant, which is often tamed and put to work.
Extension activities: Discuss the needs of domestic animals – their different diets and requirements. Compare these with the ways in which wild animals look after themselves. Discuss the meaning of the word 'wild'. Explain that a wild animal does not always mean that it is ferocious or that it will attack you.
Teachers' guide cross-references: The variety of life, pages 33, 46, 48-50.

The great escape pages 20–21

Purpose: To introduce seed dispersal and plant reproduction – showing that seeds disperse in different ways.
Notes: The pictures show acorns (which squirrels often collect and bury), blackberries and strawberries (eaten and passed out of an animals' bodies), balsam (which explodes), dandelion (the seeds have parachutes), burdock (sticks to clothes and fur), coconuts (which are in an outer case which is light enough to float). Discuss the different methods of dispersal shown.
Question for discussion: Why would it be bad if all the seeds tried to grow under the parent tree?
Extension activity: Children could look for seeds, record where they found them and try to grow them.
Teachers' guide cross-reference: Living processes, page 87.

More about living things in action

Stay well pages 8–9

Purpose: To provide discussion points related to the material in the teachers' guide.
Notes: Colourings and caffeine may be bad. Some kinds of wild berries may be harmful. Cigarettes are definitely harmful. Aspirins and vitamin pills are very harmful in large quantities. Water can be harmful if it is dirty.
Extension activity: Children could consider what else keeps us healthy – see pages 40–53.
Teachers' guide cross-references: Living processes, pages 13, 38–53.

Making us better pages 10–11

Purpose: To provide information about three of the various 'alternative' treatments available.
Extension activities: After reading this spread, ask children to explain what a homeopath or acupuncturist does.
Teachers' guide cross-reference: Living processes, page 13.

Wiping out a killer disease pages 12–13

Purpose: To look at the work of scientists and the way that, in many cases, one person is credited with what was actually the work of many; to show how inoculation has virtually wiped out a disease.

Eating habits pages 14–15

Purpose: To provide opportunities for discussion, to look at customs associated with eating.
Note: Take care over possible sensitivities, for example, children who have special diets for religious or health reasons, or who are vegetarians.
Extension activities: Get children to discuss food they eat, or do not eat. Encourage them to think about what they eat and why.
Teachers' guide cross-references: Living processes, pages 13, 14.

Breathing pages 2–3

Purpose: A discussion spread related to the activities outlined in this guide.
Note: Respiration is one of the processes of life, and should not be confused with 'breathing' (see page 103).
Extension activities: Children could write their own 'story' about how we breathe. Discuss the dangers of suffocation.
Teachers' guide cross-references: Living processes, pages 15, 56–7, 69–70.

Vital possessions pages 4–5

Purpose: To provide information about the 'vital organs' in the human body, particularly the heart.
Notes: Take care – some children may have relations who are ill or have died of heart failure. The organs are not all shown to same scale.
Extension activity: Look out for and collect news items about transplants, which the children could discuss.
Teachers' guide cross-references: Living processes, pages 14, 56–70, 103, 107–109.

The story of your blood pages 6–7

Purpose: To help children respond to the questions on page 56 of the teachers' guide.
Extension activity: Discuss general hygiene associated with cuts, and the dangers of transmitting disease, such as HIV and Hepatitis B.
Teachers' guide cross-references: Living processes, pages 15, 56 and 107.

Insect life pages 16–17

Purpose: An introduction to a life story.
Note: Dragonflies do not sting, as many children believe.
Extension activity: Children could use these pictures as a basis for a life-cycle flow diagram, thus presenting the information in a different form.
Teachers' guide cross-references: Living processes, pages 12, 77.

Did you see that! pages 18–19

Purpose: To discuss the different ways animals adapt to their environments.
Extension activity: Link the poem to work in English.
Teachers' guide cross-reference: Living things in their environment, page 55.

What plants need pages 20–21

Purpose: To look at conditions for growth.
Question for discussion: Why are some plants growing better than others? (Factors involved could include water, light, soil, weather conditions, pests.)
Extension activity: Relate this to work on the environment in a different part of the world.
Teachers' guide cross-references: Living processes, pages 12, 80–3, 86–8, 109–10.

Plants in action pages 22–23

Purpose: A 'wow' spread, to show children a variety of plants.
Pupils' book cross-references: Different plants and animals, pages 22-23; More about different plants and animals, pages 22-23; More about habitats, pages 4-5.
Teachers' guide cross-references: Living processes, pages 80–83, 86–88.

2.6 Planning your science programme in school

The following pages give examples of how two schools have planned their science programme for the whole of Key Stage 2. Planning of this kind helps to provide continuity and progression in children's learning in science. The development of such whole school programmes is discussed more fully in the *Science Co-ordinators' Handbook*.

Each plan covers the requirements for the National Curriculum at Key Stage 2 and shows which themes in the Nuffield Primary Science Teachers' Guides have been used for planning the topic in detail by the class teacher.

Example 1 (page 23)

Based in a semi-rural area this junior school has approximately 170 children on roll. There are no mixed age groups in the school. The plan provides for overlaps in order to provide opportunities for pupils to revisit concepts and build on their previous experience.

The overall curriculum is planned around topics which are history-led in the Autumn term, science-led in the Spring term and geography-led in the Summer term. Therefore, where ever possible cross-curricular links are developed, but if this becomes contrived, then subject specific mini-topics are planned. The programme only shows the Science elements taught each term.

Example 2 (page 24)

This urban school has recently reviewed its science programme in order to help encourage progression in the concepts covered and avoid repetition of the same activities. Teachers asked for guidance but also wanted the flexibility to develop the topics in a way which was appropriate to their own class.

It was also felt that some concepts, not necessarily demanded by the National Curriculum, should be covered e.g. Seasons. Therefore, suitable topics are included in the programme.

The summer term in Year 6 is free to accommodate SATs and to allow teachers time to further develop the interests of children.

Example 1

	AUTUMN TERM	SPRING TERM	SUMMER TERM
YEAR 3	The Earth and beyond/Magnetism	All about me	Service to our homes
Nuffield Primary Science Teachers' Guide	The Earth in Space 3.1, 3.2, 3.3 Electricity and magnetism 3.4	Living processes 3.1, 3.2, 3.3 The variety of life 3.2 Light 3.1	Electricity and magnetism 3.1, 3.2, 3.3 Materials 3.1 Using energy 3.2
Programme of Study †	Sc4:4a, b, c, d; Sc4:2a	Sc2: 1a; 2a, b, e, f; Sc4:3a, d	Sc3:1a, b, c; Sc4:1a, b, c
YEAR 4	Sound and music / Mechanisms	Habitats	Built environment
Nuffield Primary Science Teachers' Guide	Sound and music 3.1, 3.2 Using energy 3.3	The variety of life 3.1 Living processes 3.4 Living things in their environment 3.1, 3.2	Materials 3.2, 3.3 Using energy 3.1
Programme of Study †	Sc4:3e, f, g; Sc4:2d, e	Sc2:1b; 3a, b, c, d; 4a; Sc3:1d	Sc3:1e; 2a, b, c, d
YEAR 5	Electricity/Starting and stopping	Structures	Earth and atmosphere/ Light
Nuffield Primary Science Teachers' Guide	Electricity and magnetism 3.2, 3.3 Forces and movement 3.1, 3.2	Materials 3.1, 3.2, 3.3 Rocks, soil and weather 3.1 The variety of life 3.3	Rocks, soil and weather 3.2 The Earth in Space 3.1, 3.2, 3.3, 3.4 Light 3.2, 3.3
Programme of Study †	Sc4:1a, b, c, d; Sc4:2b, c	Sc3:1b, d; 2f; 3a, b, c, d, e	Sc3:2e; Sc4:4a, b, c, d; Sc4:3a, b, c
YEAR 6	The human body/Keeping healthy	Forces	Our environment
Nuffield Primary Science Teachers' Guide	Living processes 3.2, 3.3 The variety of life 3.2	Forces and movement 3.1, 3.2, 3.3, 3.4 Electricity and magnetism 3.4 Using energy 3.3	Living things in their environment 3.2, 3.3, 3.4
Programme of Study †	Sc2:2c, d, g, h	Sc4:2a, b, c, d, e, f, g, h	Sc2:5a, b, c, d, e

† For the purposes of these charts the references to sections of the Programme of Study have been abbreviated as follows:

Sc2 = Life Processes and Living Things
Sc3 = Materials and their Properties
Sc4 = Physical Processes

Example 2

	AUTUMN TERM		SPRING TERM		SUMMER TERM	
YEAR 3	Earth and time	Reflections and shadows	What's under our feet?	Moving things	Variety of life	Habitats
Nuffield Primary Science Teachers' Guide	The Earth in Space 3.1, 3.2	Light 3.2	Rocks, soil and weather 3.1 Living things in their environment 3.3	Forces and movement 3.1	The variety of life 3.1	Living things in their environment 3.1
Programme of Study †	Sc4:4a, b, c, d	Sc4:3a, b, c	Sc2:5e; Sc3:1d	Sc4:2a, b, c, d, e	Sc2:1a, b; 4a	Sc2:5a, b
YEAR 4	Frictional forces	Hot and cold	Materials and their properties	Sounds	Growing	Electricity
Nuffield Primary Science Teachers' Guide	Forces and movement 3.2	Using energy 3.1	Materials 3.1	Sound and music 3.1	Living processes 3.1, 3.4	Electricity and magnetism 3.1, 3.2, 3.3
Programme of Study †	Sc4:2b, c, f, g, h	Sc3:2b, c	Sc3:1a, b, e	Sc4:3e, f	Sc2:3a, b, c, d	Sc3:1c; Sc4:1a, b, c
YEAR 5	The Earth in the Solar System	Weather and its effects	Feeding relationships	Individual variation	Light sources	Sounds travelling
Nuffield Primary Science Teachers' Guides	The Earth in Space 3.1, 3.2, 3.3	Rocks, soil and weather 3.1, 3.2	Living things in their environment 3.2, 3.3	The variety of life 3.2	Light 3.1	Sound and music 3.2
Programme of Study †	Sc4:c, d	Sc3:1d, 2e	Sc2:5c, d, e	Sc2:4a; 5a	Sc4:3a, b, c, d	Sc4:3e, f, g
YEAR 6	Forces and movement	Living processes	Electricity	Materials		
Nuffield Primary Science Teachers' Guide	Forces and movement 3.3, 3.4	Living processes 3.2, 3.3	Electricity and magnetism 3.1, 3.2, 3.3	Materials 3.2, 3.3		
Programme of Study †	Sc4:2d, e, f, g, h	Sc2:2a, b, c, d, e, f, g, h	Sc4:1c, d	Sc3:2a, b, d, f; 3a, b, c, d, e		

2.7 Resources

The precise nature of the resources needed at any time will depend upon the ideas that children have and the methods of testing that they devise. The following list provides a general guide to the kind of resources that would be useful for the activities in this teachers' guide.

Selection of seeds suitable for germinating, such as cress, broad beans, bird seed, wheat, and mung etc. (Choose seeds which you can be sure have not been treated with pesticides, for instance by getting them from health food shops. Do not use red kidney beans – they are poisonous.)
Collection of leaves, fruits, seeds, and common flowers
Common plants such as dandelions
Pots for growing seeds in
Magnifying glasses
Clock or watch that records seconds
Fever strip thermometers
Stethoscopes
Model skeletons, collections of bones, X-ray plates
Food packages, pictures of food, plants and animals
Venn diagram circles for sorting and classifying
Books about the human body, animals and plants
Video tapes showing movement of vertebrates
Leaflets about healthy eating – these are available free from many stores.
Audio-visual packages about sex education (optional)

2.8 Warnings

Activities which need particular care are indicated by this symbol in the margin. Everything possible should be done to ensure the safety of the children during their investigations. You should consult any guidelines produced by your own Local Education Authority and, if your school or LEA is a member, by CLEAPSS. See also the Association for Science Education publication *Be safe! some aspects of safety in school science and technology for Key Stages 1 and 2* (2nd edition, 1990). This contains more detailed advice than can be included here.

The points listed below require particular attention.

Take care that children do not pick wild flowers. Many are protected species.

Much of the work about the body and health needs to be tackled with great care, as it often involves value judgements which could derive from a particular cultural perspective, for example about what constitutes a healthy diet. We need to make it clear to children that we are not talking about one type of diet (such as a western diet), but that we are talking about principles which can be applied more generally. Teachers need to be knowledgeable about the dietary requirements of the children they are teaching, which may be based on cultural traditions, moral judgements, or religion.

Sensitivity needs to be exercised when making comparisons between children about such things as skin colour, height, the speed they can run, and so on; very few children like being singled out in any way. When talking about families, remember that many children may come from one-parent families or be adopted.

Ideas about hygiene will vary considerably between groups of people and may depend on the facilities they have available to them.

When carrying out investigations about lung capacity, children should not blow down the same tube or balloon unless it has been disinfected.

Glass clinical thermometers are not suitable for use in schools as children could easily bite on them. Liquid crystal forehead thermometers should be used instead.

When measuring breathing rate, take care that children do not hyperventilate or hold their breath. It is usually better if they measure their friends' breathing rates to help to prevent this from happening.

Before embarking on a programme of sex education, consult your school guidelines. It is usual for the school governors to approve any such programme before it is adopted.

CHAPTER 3

Exploring living processes

Theme organizer

LIVING PROCESSES

HOW DO WE KNOW IF IT IS ALIVE?

3.1

All living things have the potential to carry out all of the following processes at some stage in their life: respiration, reproduction, feeding, excretion, movement, reaction to stimuli, growth and development.

There is a wide variety of life, which includes plants and animals.

Living things are distinguished from non-living things by their ability to carry out certain processes.

*All living things are made of cells.

KEEPING HEALTHY

3.2

Many factors, such as diet and exercise, affect the health of our bodies.

Some things, such as drugs, alcohol and tobacco, can harm our health.

THE HUMAN BODY

3.3

The human body is made up of organs and organ systems which have specific functions and interact with each other.

Human beings are mammals.

PLANTS

3.4

Plants form one group of living things. This group includes both flowering plants and non-flowering plants.

Plants need light, water, carbon dioxide, oxygen and nutrients to grow.

*Plants can make food from water and carbon dioxide in the presence of light and chlorophyll. This process is called photosynthesis.

(*Asterisks indicate ideas which will be developed more fully in later key stages.)

How do we know if it is alive?

AREAS FOR INVESTIGATION

◆ Characteristics of living and non-living things.

◆ Life processes common to living things.

(see also *Variety of Life.*)

KEY IDEAS

◆ There is a wide variety of life, which includes plants and animals.

◆ All living things have the potential to carry out all of the following processes at some stage in their life: respiration, reproduction, feeding, excretion, movement, reaction to stimuli, growth and development.

◆ *All living things are made of cells.

(*Asterisks indicate ideas which will be developed more fully in later key stages.)

A LOOK AT How do we know if it is alive?

Living things respire, feed, excrete, move, sense their surroundings, grow and reproduce. These processes distinguish them from non-living things.

In general, children will not distinguish between living and non-living things by the presence or absence of these characteristic processes. Observation of various living organisms may help children to identify some of these processes as common to all living things and, on the basis of these processes, enable them to distinguish between living and non-living things.

Finding out children's ideas

■ STARTER ACTIVITIES

Deciding whether objects are living, never lived or once living

Give the children a group of objects to classify into these three groups. Select different items including plants, animals, and manufactured and natural objects. For example:

- ◆ a selection of plants
- ◆ animals such as 'minibeasts', or pictures of animals
- ◆ a plastic bowl
- ◆ a metal spoon
- ◆ an apple
- ◆ a toy car
- ◆ a rock
- ◆ seeds

 Q *Look at each one separately: is it living, never lived or once living? Why? (Think of more than one reason if possible.)*

Ask the children to record their findings in writing, or by giving verbal reasons for placing each item in a category. How do the children define what is alive? Are they consistent?

Children's ideas

Children of primary school age do not necessarily have a clear idea about whether things are living, once living or never lived and, when asked to classify a set of objects, they may use very different reasons from those given by adults. Having initially decided on their reasons for a classification, they are often remarkably consistent in applying them to a whole set of objects, even when their reasons do not appear to make much sense. For example, a child who decided that things are 'not living' if you can 'buy them in a shop' continued to apply these criteria rigorously, deciding that plants and animals are 'not living' because it is possible to buy both of these in shops! It would appear that having decided on criteria at the beginning of a classification exercise many children are reluctant to change their ideas and adopt more useful criteria later in an exercise.

Children give many different reasons in their attempts at classification into living, never lived or once living, and may include some of the following.

Things are said to be living because:

> *We use them now.*
> *We have them in our houses.*
> *They feel hard.*
> *They move.*
> *They have homes.*
> *They have faces.*

They also give as a reason that a thing 'lives' somewhere, for example:

> *A spoon lives in the drawer.*

Things are said to be never lived because:

> *They feel hard.*
> *They have holes in them.*
> *They are broken.*
> *I've never seen one before!*

They are said to be once living because:

> *We used to have them.*
> *You can kill them – they'll never live.*
>
> (This child meant that an insect would never live if trodden on!)

31

Some children do give biological reasons, although these are mainly restricted to growing, breathing or eating.

Here are some examples of children's reasons for classifying particular things.

◆ A metal spoon:

Once living

Because it was made, it wasn't rusty, now it's become rusty and it's not alive.

Never lived

It has no eyes, hair, arms, legs.

◆ An apple:

Never lived

It has no brain, it doesn't go to school.

Even when children decide on the correct categories when classifying, they are not necessarily using biological criteria to make their decisions. For example:

◆ An animal:

Living

I have seen them on TV.

They eat too much!

They have got fur.

Children towards the end of Key Stage 2 are more likely to be able to give more sophisticated reasons. For example:

◆ An animal:

Living

They breathe, they've got eyes to see.

Living

They move, breathe and grow.

It is possible that children's criteria for deciding whether things are 'living' develop through the following stages.

1 Children appear to have no concept of what is alive, and may offer, as criteria, observable features, for example:

It is made of metal, it is broken.

2 Children associate people's use of an object with living, for example:

Spoons are alive because we use them.

3 Children suggest that things which move are alive.

4 Children suggest that things which are like humans are alive, for example:

They have eyes and legs like me.

5 Children consider that only animals are alive.

6 The scientific explanation – both animals and plants are alive.

Helping children to develop their ideas

The chart opposite shows how you can help children to develop their ideas from starting points which have given rise to different ideas.

The centre rectangle contains a starter question.

The surrounding 'thought bubbles' contain the sorts of ideas expressed by children.

The further ring of rectangles contains questions posed by teachers in response to the ideas expressed by the children. These questions are meant to prompt children to think about their ideas.

The outer ovals indicate ways in which the children might respond to the teacher's questions.

Some of the shapes have been left blank, as a sign that other ideas may be encountered and other ways of helping children to develop their ideas may be tried.

1 Distinguishing between living and non-living things

Get the children to draw a set of things which they think are alive and a set of things which they think are not alive. They may find this exercise much easier than the one suggested as a starter activity, where they are asked to classify a varied set of given objects.

For living things, children will often choose to draw animals, particularly mammals, rather than plants. They will also tend to draw things with which they are familiar, such as common pets, people and so on, which they can confidently say are living or non-living.

When they have drawn their sets, ask the children to give reasons for their decisions. Get them to discuss their results, either in pairs or in a larger group. You could ask:

Q *Do you agree with your friends' sets?*
Have they given the same reasons as you did for saying that things are living or non-living?

The children could compile a class list of living and non-living things.

Sorting and classifying activities can help children to clarify their thinking, to work co-operatively and to exchange ideas. At a simple level these can be straightforward, for example

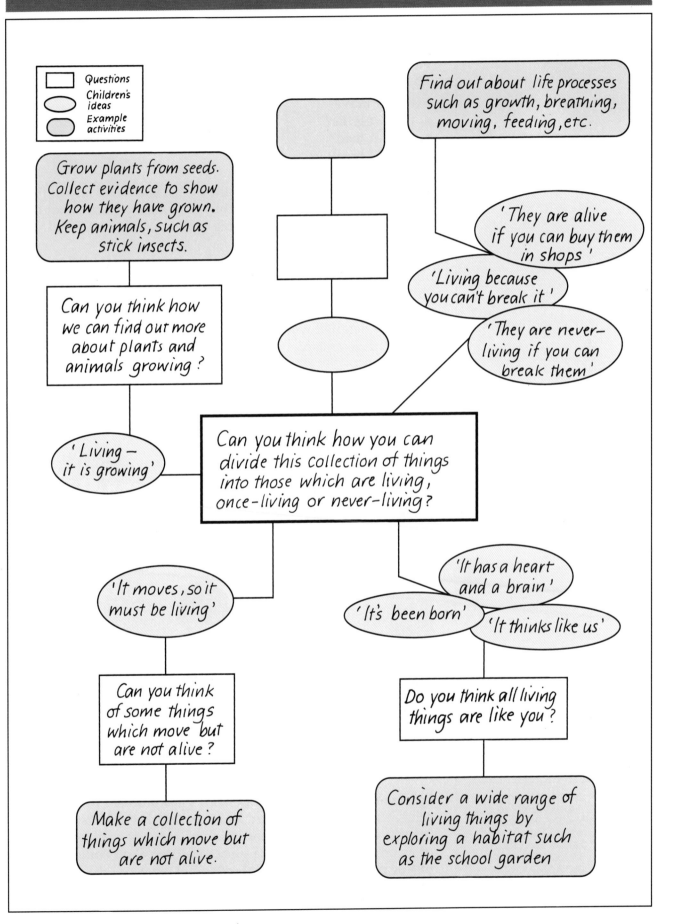

Questions

Children's ideas

Example activities

Find out about life processes such as growth, breathing, moving, feeding, etc.

Grow plants from seeds. Collect evidence to show how they have grown. Keep animals, such as stick insects.

'They are alive if you can buy them in shops'

'Living because you can't break it'

'They are never-living if you can break them'

Can you think how we can find out more about plants and animals growing?

'Living — it is growing'

Can you think how you can divide this collection of things into those which are living, once-living or never-living?

'It moves, so it must be living'

'It has a heart and a brain'

'It's been born'

'It thinks like us'

Can you think of some things which move but are not alive?

Do you think all living things are like you?

Make a collection of things which move but are not alive.

Consider a wide range of living things by exploring a habitat such as the school garden sorting objects into two sets by means of Venn diagrams and, at a higher level, by using 'decision trees'.

Computer programs which allow children to make up their own 'decision trees', or keys for classification, are useful in this work. Children could list their criteria on a computer with a suitable database program, and then use them for classification. For example:

◆ Can it move?
◆ Does it grow?
◆ Does it feed?
◆ Does it breathe?

Children may find it hard to believe that plants do any of these things apart from growing, so they may need to think about the criteria for deciding if something is living and is a plant.

You could ask the children to go back to the original group of objects which they classified as a starter activity. Do the children still use the same criteria? Get them to compare their responses. Alternatively, wait until the children have carried out more detailed work on life processes before asking them to repeat this exercise.

2 Exploring the environment

Children could investigate a piece of ground near to their school. An ideal area would be one which has plants, animals (insects and other 'minibeasts'), some rocks or pebbles, pieces of wood and possibly some pieces of litter. (You could 'plant' one or two items of litter if they do not exist.)

COVER CUTS AND ABRASIONS BEFORE STARTING WORK, AND WASH HANDS AFTERWARDS. CHILDREN SHOULD WEAR RUBBER GLOVES (OR PLASTIC BAGS) ON THEIR HANDS WHEN COLLECTING LITTER

Ask the children to explore the area of ground, noting down or drawing the objects they find under headings such as 'Living', 'Once living', 'Never living', 'Don't know'. This may help the children to realize that plants are living things, even though their characteristics may not be as obvious as those of animals. (Note that some litter, such an as apple core, is 'not once living', while things like empty crisp packets are 'never living'.)

This could lead to interesting discussions about caring for the environment, and why it is both inappropriate and harmful to drop litter. You may be surprised to find that many children believe trees to be non-living, especially in winter; after all, 'The trees are dead' is an expression in common usage. Children may interpret this to mean that trees are no longer alive (once-living). If they are dead, it is therefore not destructive to break off branches! If this work is carried out in the winter, children could investigate what we mean by 'plants dying' in the winter. If they really die, how do they reappear the following year? This could lead to work on plant life cycles and on deciduous and evergreen trees.

This activity could be linked with others in *Living things in their environment*.

Keeping healthy

AREAS FOR INVESTIGATION

◆ The ways in which we keep ourselves healthy.

◆ Healthy eating and a balanced diet.

◆ Effects of harmful substances.

KEY IDEAS

◆ Many factors, such as diet and exercise, affect the health of our bodies.

◆ Some things, such as drugs, alcohol and tobacco, can harm our health.

A LOOK AT
keeping healthy

To keep ourselves healthy we need to take regular exercise, eat a balanced diet and avoid certain substances.

Many health problems associated with an unhealthy lifestyle become apparent only over time. Adopting a healthy diet and taking exercise from when we are young may save us from suffering some health problems later on.

A well-balanced diet provides the body with protein for growth and repair, carbohydrates and fats for energy, fibre to stimulate the digestive system, and vitamins and minerals to help body processes.

Drugs can be very helpful to us. We use them, often in small amounts, as medicines, and in alcoholic drinks, tea and coffee. The over-use of drugs is very harmful to our health, and can cause addiction. Certain drugs are dangerous even at the first dose. It is very important to distinguish between the use and the abuse of drugs.

Smoking in any form puts our health at risk. Many diseases are much more common among smokers than among non-smokers; for example, smokers are more likely to suffer from heart disease, bronchitis and various forms of cancer. Giving up smoking reduces the risk of these diseases, and generally increases fitness.

We can raise our general level of fitness by taking regular exercise, which gives us more efficient breathing and greater lung capacity, better circulation and a stronger heart.

Finding out children's ideas
■ STARTER ACTIVITIES

1 What keeps us healthy?

To discover children's ideas of what it means to lead a healthy life, you could ask them to draw four things which have to do with keeping healthy. This exercise will be more interesting if you do not discuss possible responses with the children first. Get them to annotate their drawings, if they are able to do this.

Then ask the children whether they think that keeping healthy is mainly due to the food we eat, or if they attribute it to a wider range of factors.

You could get children to think of a wider range of factors which contribute to healthy living. Give them a list such as the copiable one opposite.

Ask:

 Which of these things help us to keep healthy? Draw a ring round them.
What are your reasons for choosing them?

Also ask them to make a list of things they think may be harmful to their health, and to give reasons for their responses.

During each activity the children could write down their reasons or discuss them with other children.

2 Healthy eating

Ask children to draw a picture of a healthy and a not-so-healthy meal.

You could give them a copy of page 42 on which they can draw the two meals.

Ask the children to decide which of the following are healthy foods:

lettuce	cola	burgers
sugar	orange juice	sweets
bread	apples	crisps
meat	rice	biscuits
chips	potatoes	pasta

The children may wish to qualify their responses. For example, they may say that some meat such as lean chicken is healthy, but burgers and fatty meat are less healthy.

arguing

....

....

swimming

....

....

watching television

....

....

sleeping

....

....

feeling happy

....

....

smoking

....

....

eating

....

....

fighting

....

....

playing with friends

....

....

reading

....

....

laughing

....

....

running

....

....

3.2

unhealthy meal

healthy meal

NUFFIELD PRIMARY SCIENCE: LIVING PROCESSES

Children's ideas

1 Ideas about what keeps us healthy

Many children appear to think that the state of our health is mainly to be attributed to the food we eat. When asked to draw four things which have to do with keeping healthy, many children will think only (or mainly) in terms of food. Typical examples of healthy food are carrots, bananas, tomatoes, brown bread, apples, salad and grapes. Examples are shown here.

Some children may suggest a wider range of factors, such as exercise of various kinds, but this is less common.

Children often seem to suggest adult forms of exercise, and do not think of the things that children do, such as running, walking, playing, riding a bike or swimming.

Surprisingly, some children may shake their heads vigorously or give an emphatic 'no' when asked if eating is to do with

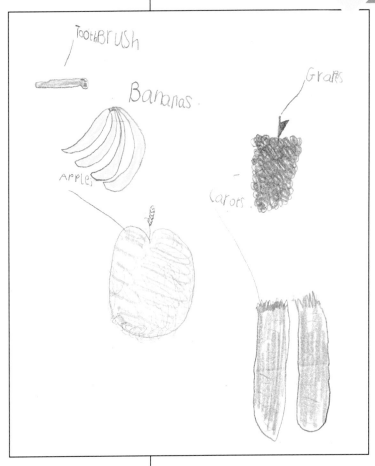

keeping healthy. This may be because some children have negative attitudes towards food and eating because of media pressure to slim.

Children commonly feel that arguing, smoking and fighting are not healthy activities. 'Watching television' can be debatable, depending on whether the children see this as an opportunity for them to relax and to learn something new, or as mere inactivity. It is always worth pressing children to give reasons for their responses.

2 Ideas about healthy eating

Children seem to be well aware of which foods are not particularly healthy – sweets, chips, burgers, biscuits and so on – but, rather as with adults, this does not stop them enjoying these. When asked to draw healthy and unhealthy food, many children will suggest that fruit and vegetables are healthy food.

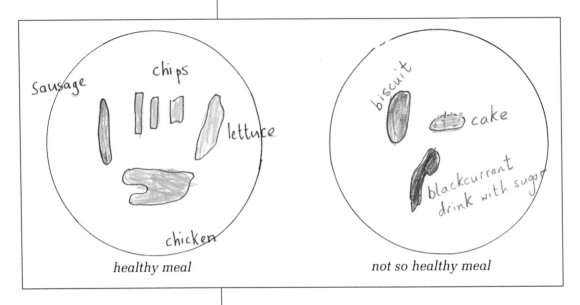

healthy meal   *not so healthy meal*

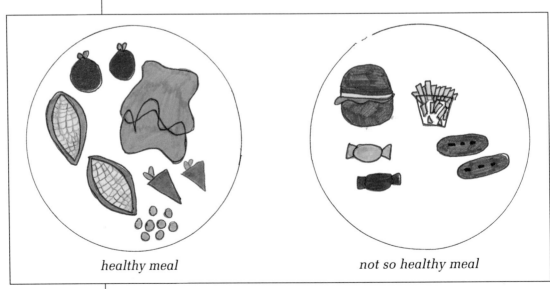

healthy meal   *not so healthy meal*

A few children will be able to describe some constituents of foods such as proteins and calcium. They might be aware that a balanced diet is healthier than eating particular types of food.

I am thinking about good Food and bad Food. we eat Food because it is healthy.

I eat different food Because Some things have calcium In and Some other Things have Protein and other things have Sugar In and Thats good Because you get all diffrent Stuf Inside You and If you eat Just one Thing you Would Just get one thing Inside You.

X

rigt

rong

Helping children to develop their ideas

The chart opposite shows how you can help children to develop their ideas from starting points which have given rise to different ideas.

The centre rectangle contains a starter question.

The surrounding 'thought bubbles' contain the sorts of ideas expressed by children.

The further ring of rectangles contains questions posed by teachers in response to the ideas expressed by the children. These questions are meant to prompt children to think about their ideas.

The outer ovals indicate ways in which the children might respond to the teacher's questions.

Some of the shapes have been left blank, as a sign that other ideas may be encountered and other ways of helping children to develop their ideas may be tried.

1 What keeps us healthy?

AT 1   GENERAL

Children will undoubtedly have ideas for their own investigations into keeping healthy. They could start by compiling a list of questions they want answered. This could be followed by discussing how they could find out some of the answers for themselves. Some of the following suggestions may be helpful.

a What we do to keep healthy

Ask the children to draw a person. On one side of the drawing ask them to write the factors which keep the person healthy. Ask them to write down on the other side of the drawing all the things which the person might do to make him or herself unhealthy.

b A healthy day

As an introduction to finding out more about ways to lead a healthier life, children could keep a record of one day (24 hours), noting down all the things they do which keep them healthy: for example, ways of keeping clean and of keeping safe, exercise, food, rest, relaxation, playing with friends and so on. The following questions may help to get them started:

 What things can you do to keep yourself clean, safe and healthy?
Who helps you to do some of these things?

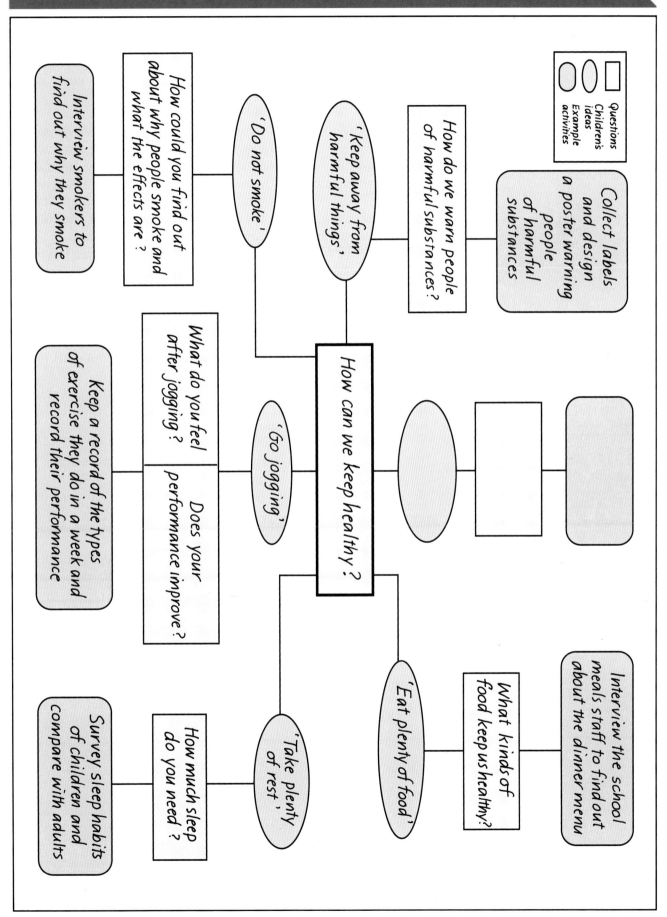

Children could sort a set of cards or pictures into a sequence to make up a healthy day. Or they could draw their own pictures of the things they do during the course of one day, and then decide which of these are essential parts of a healthy lifestyle.

This work may involve reference to secondary sources such as videos, books, and computer programs which enable you to devise a well-balanced meal, and consulting experts such as the school nurse or health visitor.

To keep healthy we not only need to avoid harmful substances, we also need protection from disease. Scientific discoveries over many years have led to the elimination of many diseases which were fatal in childhood. Children could find out about some of the injections they have been given. *More about living things in action* gives information about some of the people who have made major discoveries about immunization. Children could also use *More about living things in action* to find out about some alternative medical practitioners.

Children could be asked to think about their school and how it could be made into a more health-promoting place. Ask them to think about food, exercise, cleanliness, safety, friendliness and so on. They could then turn their findings into a wall display, or make a poster on a subject such as:

'Our school is a healthy place to be because ...'
'Our school would be a more healthy place if ...'

Children could work in pairs or in small groups, producing a display each or contributing to a large one.

c Harmful substances

Children could make a list of the things which they know can be harmful to health. One suggestion is likely to be drugs.

Children could use *More about living things in action* to help them discuss their ideas about harmful substances.

This will need careful handling so that children become aware of the difference between the use and abuse of drugs, and know that not all drugs are harmful – indeed, many are lifesaving. There may be children in the class who are dependent on drugs to keep them alive, for example diabetics.

Encourage the children to think not only of things which are normally known as drugs, but of other substances which may have harmful effects. These might include alcohol, caffeine, food additives, and excessive amounts of sugar.

Ask the children to think of how they could find out more about harmful substances. They may suggest reference to secondary sources such as books and videos, looking at food labels, or inviting experts into school so the children can question them.

The children could design their own posters warning others to avoid substances which can damage health.

pb

! SOME CHILDREN TAKE MEDICATION

AT 1 COMMUNICATING

d Smoking

It appears that children are aware that smoking is harmful to health. Most children will know people who smoke and may be puzzled that they are doing something which everyone knows to be harmful. Children may need to be made aware that most of the people who start smoking do so when they are as young as twelve or thirteen, and then find it extremely difficult to stop.

Get the children to think of all the reasons for people starting smoking in the first place. They could discuss their ideas in groups. Ask:

Q *Why do you think people start smoking?*

AT 1 HYPOTHESIZING

This could lead to discussions of other harmful substances and what motivates people to take them.

You could use role play to get the children to think of ways of dealing with the pressures their peers may put on them to smoke or take drugs. For example,

> *'Come on – everyone else is, why don't you try it?'*

could be countered by

> 'I don't need to be like everyone else. I prefer to think things out for myself.'

Alternatively, the children could devise a cartoon strip story about some children who were offered some cigarettes and how they reacted.

e Looking after our lungs

It may be useful to link this work with that in 'The human body' (pages 69-71).

Ask the children to think about how important our lungs are to us. Many children will have experienced difficulty in breathing at some time, when they were frightened, or during a bad cold or an asthma attack, for example.

Children could think about the things that can damage our lungs and make it very difficult to breathe. Ask them:

Q *How can we keep our lungs healthy?*
What kind of things may damage our lungs?

This can be followed up by thinking about the need for clean air.

Q *Why do you think cyclists in big cities, builders, painters and so on wear masks over their noses and mouths?*

Listen to air pollution reports on the radio and ask:

Q *What might contribute to air pollution?*
Do you know about some of the things which are being done to make the air cleaner?
What kinds of places are the most polluted?
How can we look after our lungs?

f Looking after our hearts

It may be useful to link this work with that in 'The human body' (pages 71-72).

Q *How do you think we can keep our hearts healthy?*

Ask for children's ideas of things that contribute to heart disease. Do they know how it can be made less likely? Preventive measures may include avoiding too much fatty food, not smoking, and taking regular exercise.

g Exercise and health

Ask the children to keep a 24-hour diary, marking in all the times when they take exercise. The children could choose their own code for showing rest, light exercise and more vigorous exercise. They could show their findings as a series of cartoon drawings.

Children could discuss the types of exercise which they prefer, and use a computer to compile a graph of the class findings, to show which are the most popular types of exercise.

h Group activities

The following ideas could be used for group discussions.

Get the children to think about healthy people and the things that keep them healthy.

 What kind of things do you think healthy people do?
What kind of things do you think healthy people avoid?

They could devise a message, perhaps a poster, to tell people how they could become more healthy.

Get the children to discuss the items in the list on page 41. It would be easier if the words were put on separate cards so that the children could talk about them one at a time, sorting them into the appropriate sets: 'keeps us healthy' and 'doesn't keep us healthy'. You could share the word cards between a group of children, allowing individual children to talk about the words on their cards, and to sort them into the two sets. The rest of the children can say whether they agree or disagree, giving their reasons.

Get all children to share their findings with each other, deciding which of the things healthy people do – some of the time, all of the time or never.

It should be made clear to children that poor health is not necessarily due to an unhealthy lifestyle; but on the other hand adopting a more healthy lifestyle *can* help to protect people from ailments which result directly from poor eating, lack of exercise, smoking, and so on.

2 Healthy eating

a Eating in school

To find out more about healthy eating, children could think about the kind of food they eat at school. If the school has a tuck shop, ask:

 What kind of things do they sell there?
Are all these things healthy?

If the school does not have a tuck shop, why was it decided not to have one?

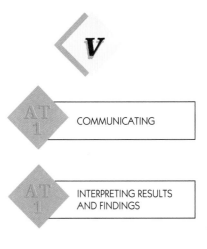

COMMUNICATING

INTERPRETING RESULTS AND FINDINGS

AT 1 COMMUNICATING

Q *Do you think it is a good idea to have a tuck shop?*

The children could interview teachers and children in the school to ask them what they think about this. They could report their findings to the class.

Get the children to think of possible advantages and disadvantages of having a tuck shop.

The children could set up a 'healthy eating' tuck shop for one week. Ask them:

Q *What kind of food could be served?*
How could the food be stored and kept fresh?
How should the food be handled?

The children could use a computer to keep, and display, a record of the most popular choices.

Information about healthy eating can be found in *Living things in action.*

b School lunches

You could ask the children for their thoughts about lunches.

Q *Do you bring a packed lunch?*
Do you prefer packed lunches to eating school lunches?
What kind of food do you have in your lunch?
Who decides what kind of lunch you have?
Do your parents agree with you about the kind of food you should eat?
What are the most popular lunches on the menu in the school canteen?
How does the cook decide on the menu?

If the school has its own cook on the premises, perhaps he or she might be interviewed by the children. The findings could be reported back to the class.

Q *Where does the food come from?*
How is it kept fresh?
What care do the cooks have to take when handling the food?
How does the cook ensure that the children have a balanced meal?
If the meals are not cooked on the school premises, where do they come from?
How is the food kept fresh and/or hot?
How is the menu decided?

c Grouping foods

Get the children to think about ways of grouping foods.

Give them a selection of pictures, packages, examples of different foods, and ask them to think of ways of sorting them into different groups. Let them devise their own groups such as fruits, vegetables, cereals, sweets, cakes, and so on.

The children are probably not familiar with the scientific grouping of food into fats, proteins and carbohydrates. These groups are introduced in *More about using energy*.

Talking to such people as the school cook, the health advisory teacher or the health visitor, or referring to secondary sources, will also give the children the opportunity to find out about ways of grouping foods.

You may find it more appropriate to leave the idea of scientific groupings until Key Stage 3 and to use groupings such as cereals, dairy foods, vegetables, pulses and so on.

A useful way of getting children to apply their knowledge of food groupings is to ask them to devise a balanced meal, either from their own ideas or chosen from a menu.

Ask them to give reasons for their choices.

Children could draw the meal which they ate the previous evening.

 Where do you think the food came from?
How was it cooked?
Which parts of the meal were particularly healthy?

Caution is needed here in dealing with food cooked in different ways. Teachers need to be particularly aware of the dietary customs of the children in their class, so that children are not made to feel that the food traditional to their culture is in any way inferior to a western diet. It may on the contrary be more healthy. Children will be less willing to talk about their home cooking if they feel that this will be treated as exotic, as most of them like to feel that they are conforming to the norm. Anyway, most diets consist of similar basic foods, the main difference being the way in which these are cooked.

Children could use *Living things in action*, *More about living things in action*, *Using energy*, and *More about using energy* to find out more about eating and health.

The human body

AREAS FOR INVESTIGATION

◆ The human digestive system.

◆ Circulation and breathing.

◆ Bones and muscles of the human body.

◆ Reproduction and growth.

◆ This theme can be linked with work in 'Keeping healthy' (page 38).

KEY IDEAS

◆ The human body is made up of organs and organ systems which have specific functions and interact with each other.

◆ Humans beings are mammals.

A LOOK AT
the human body

The body needs food for growth and repair and as a source of energy. Nutrients from food are absorbed by the body as food passes down the digestive tract, a continuous tube stretching from the mouth to the anus. Digestion begins with the mechanical and chemical breakdown of food in the mouth. After passing through the gullet the breakdown continues in the stomach. The food travels on to the small intestine, where nutrients pass through the intestine wall into the blood. What remains moves from the small intestine to the large intestine and out of the body as faeces, through the anus.

A constant supply of oxygen is needed by the body to enable it to stay alive. During breathing, air is taken down the windpipe and into the lungs, where oxygen is taken from it. The blood carries oxygen to all parts of the body where it is used in releasing energy; the waste products of this release are carbon dioxide and water, which are returned to the lungs by the blood.

The heart is a large muscle that pumps blood around the body continuously. Blood travels away from the heart in arteries, and returns to the heart in veins. The heart has two sides, the right side circulating blood through the lungs so that it can be oxygenated, and the left sending oxygenated blood to the rest of the body.

Muscles, bones and joints provide the body with a supportive structure that allows flexibility of movement.

Movement is controlled by muscles, which are arranged in pairs. For example, a set of muscles on one side of your arm bends your elbow, and a set on the other side straightens it.

The muscles in the arms are under our conscious control, and are called voluntary muscles.

There are other muscles in the body over which we do not have conscious control. These are called involuntary muscles; examples are the heart and the muscles of the digestive tract.

Finding out children's ideas

STARTER ACTIVITIES

The copiable sheet on page 58 which shows an outline of the human body may be helpful for some children in the following activities.

1 Digestion

To find out children's ideas about digestion, ask:

 What do you think happens to food and drink inside your body?

Ask the children to draw a picture, annotating it to explain their ideas in more detail, or give them an outline drawing of a human body so that they can add to it, to show what they think happens to food and drink.

Children may think that food and drink goes into their stomach and then 'disappears', 'goes into the blood', or 'goes to your legs'; or they may have a more sophisticated explanation involving the digestive system.

Ask questions to discover whether they understand the word 'stomach' as it is used in a biological sense, or if they use it to refer to the abdominal area in general.

Try to find out what children understand about the body's need for food. Their view of food and eating may be more recreational than biological – that is, eating favourite foods, such as ice cream, sweets, and so on, may simply be seen as a pleasurable activity in its own right, with no connections made to bodily need. To see if this is the case, you could simply ask:

 Why do you need to eat?

2 Circulation and breathing

Some of the following questions may be useful for finding out what children think about these matters.

 What does the blood do?
Where is your heart?
What do you think happens to the air you breathe in?
How does blood move round the body? What makes it move?
Where do you think your lungs are?

Children could mark on an outline drawing of a body where they think their heart and lungs are. They could also add blood vessels to the drawing. This may show whether they are aware of blood being pumped through arteries and veins by the heart.

3 Bones and muscles

Ask the children some of the following questions:

> *What do your bones do?*
> *Can you name any of the bones in your body?*
> *Where are your muscles?*
> *How do you move different parts of your body? How can you bend your arm, for example?*

Give the children time to discuss their ideas. They could also show these ideas in a drawing.

4 Growth and reproduction

These two questions form a useful starting point for work on growth and reproduction. Give the children the opportunity to make an individual response by drawing and writing their answers before they are asked to share them with others.

> *Where do you think living things come from?*
> *Where do you think babies grow before they are born?*

Children's ideas

1 Ideas about digestion

On the whole, children at Key Stages 1 and 2 do not have a clear idea of the process of digestion. Younger children tend to think that the digestive system consists of a tube from the mouth which goes into the stomach and stops there, or that food simply goes into the body. From the stomach, it goes to your muscles, disappears, goes into your blood and so on.

Can you draw a picture to show what happens to food and drink inside your body?

When young children draw pictures to illustrate their ideas about digestion, they frequently represent food 'whole'. In the drawing on the next page, the child has drawn bread as a whole loaf travelling down the gullet into the stomach and finally out of the body. Only further questioning will reveal whether the child actually thinks that food remains intact inside the body, or simply wishes to represent it in a recognizable way.

Some children, especially older juniors, think that food and drink go to different places inside the

When I go to the toilet all the food in my body comes out

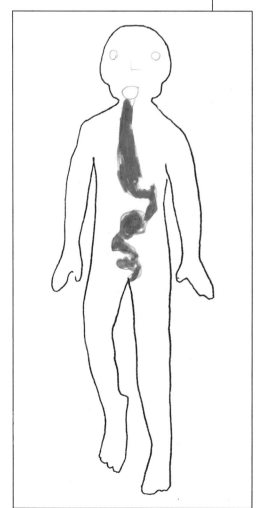

body. To illustrate this, they may draw two tubes going into separate 'bags', which they often refer to as the 'food bag' and 'drink bag'. This may be because they have heard people saying that food or drink has 'gone down the wrong way'! Alternatively, children may think that food and drink take different routes through the body because they appear to come out in different places.

It goes into different parts.

Other children have the more accurate idea that the digestive system is a continuous tube from the mouth to the anus, as this example shows.

Many children do not appear to associate 'going to the toilet' with the process of digestion, but think of it as a separate process. They do not appear to be clear about the end processes of digestion, or if they are they think of only one outcome; for example:

> *The food goes into your blood.*
> *It goes to your muscles.*
> *It comes out when you go to the toilet.*

Only children in Years 5 or 6 appear to have some knowledge of the changes which food undergoes as it passes along the alimentary canal. Even then, they rarely understand the changes made to food before its nutritive constituents are carried by the blood to all parts of the body.

2 Circulation and breathing

Children usually know the position of those parts of the body which they can see, feel or hear. Thus they are generally more aware of the position of their heart than of their lungs. The use of the term 'chest' to refer to lungs in everyday conversations may also confuse some children.

Can you draw a picture to show where your heart is?

What does your heart do?

My Heart keeps beating

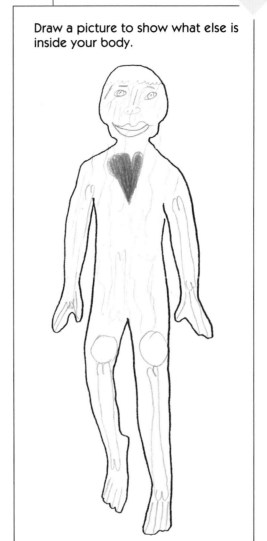

Draw a picture to show what else is inside your body.

Most children are able to locate the heart in roughly the right place on a drawing of the human body, but represent it rather like a Valentine heart, as the examples above show.

Some children think of the body as an empty cavity which is filled with blood – when they cut themselves, the blood simply runs out! The drawing above left shows the body coloured red to show how it is completely filled with blood.

Most children at this stage refer to all blood vessels as 'veins' and appear to be unfamiliar with the word 'arteries', or the fact that blood is carried from the heart by arteries and returns through the veins. Only a minority of children seem to be aware of the circulation of the blood, or that breathing is connected in any way with the function of the heart.

Very few children have well developed ideas about the processes involved in breathing or what happens to the air which they breathe in. Most children know that they 'will die if they do not have air', but appear to think that the air which we breathe in simply 'comes out'. Very few are able to locate lungs on a drawing of the human body.

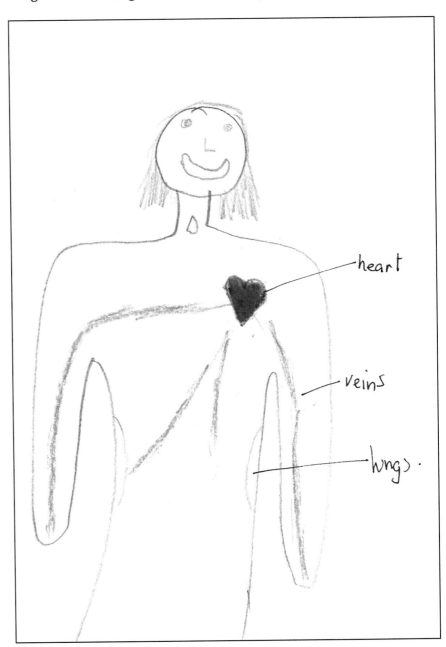

Here are some replies children made when asked what they thought happens to the air which they breathe in.

> *It goes down your body.*
> *It changes into bad air.*
> *The air stops.*

These responses demonstrate that these children do not have a clear idea about the process of breathing, or the parts of the body which are used for it.

Some children are aware of some of the gases which play a part in respiration.

It goes in and we let out carbon dioxide like plants do – let out oxygen.

When you breathe out air, the trees swallow it and return it as oxygen.

Few children are aware of oxygen from the lungs, and carbon dioxide from processes in the body, being circulated by the blood. The remark below does show some understanding of this; but is a relatively rare instance.

It goes into your lungs – it comes out of these kind of tubes – it goes into your heart and then into your blood.

3 Bones, muscles and support

Children tend to think of the body as an empty cavity which contains various unconnected organs, bones and blood.

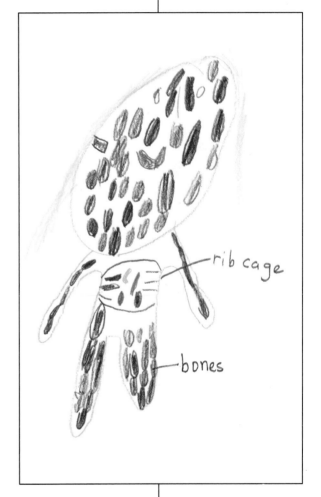

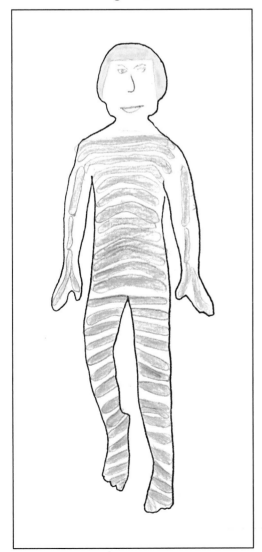

When asked to explain where their muscles are, the majority of children think of their arms and possibly legs, but do not appear to recognize that all movements of the body involve muscles.

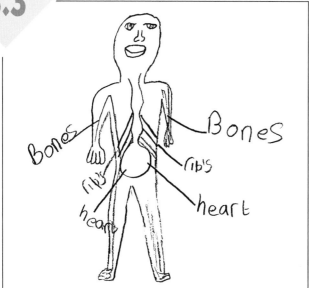

In the same way, children are aware of bones being present in their arms and legs, and possibly of their ribs and skull, but often do not include either the spine or the pelvis. Children often represent bones rather like the ones they may see in cartoon drawings, or the stereotypical dog bone, with large bulbous ends, and separate from each other. The bones are often drawn in straight rows going across the body. Even the skull can be represented in this way: as a collection of many bones together, which do not differ in appearance from the bones in the rest of the body.

4 Growth and reproduction

Children's ideas about human reproduction have been discussed by Susan Carey in *Conceptual change in childhood* (MIT Press, Cambridge, Mass., 1985). Some of her findings are presented here.

Children's ideas can be divided into the following main stages.

1 Very young children find it hard to come to terms with the idea that at one time they did not exist. The first step in understanding human reproduction is therefore coming to an understanding of the transition from non-existence to existence. Children's thoughts at this stage may be about where they were before they were born rather than how they came into existence.

2 At the next stage, children tend to think of 'babies being made' in the same way as other things are made – that is, manufactured. They do not attribute biological properties to this process.

3 At the third stage children are aware that a mother and father are involved in the process, but may be more concerned with the relationship between the two people and the baby growing in the mother's 'tummy' rather than the physical process of reproduction.

4 At this stage children have a model which includes a 'seed' from the father and an 'egg' from the mother. Many children tend to think of these rather like the seeds and eggs they are familiar with, that is, a seed from a plant and a hen's egg. They are aware that the seed is needed so that the egg will grow and hatch; for example:

The seed makes the egg grow.

One child said,

> It's just like plants; if you plant a seed a flower will grow.
> It's a special kind of seed, that makes an egg hatch.

Teacher   *Why must the seed touch the egg for the baby to grow?*

Child   *The egg won't hatch.*

5   At this stage children have come across words such as 'fertilization' and have some understanding of what they mean, although they have not yet come to a full understanding of the processes involved. For example:

Teacher   *What does 'fertilize' mean?*

Child   *Kind of give it food and things like that.*

Teacher   *How is it that the baby starts growing when the sperm goes into the egg?*

Child   *I guess when it gets in there it just does something to the egg, and it makes it start growing.*

By the end of Key Stage 2, children may be aware of the role of parents to have intercourse and of the body processes which then take over. Younger children may not make this distinction and may not perceive 'having babies' as in any way intentional. It is important that children understand that the role played by the mother and father in the reproductive process is both biological and social.

Helping children to develop their ideas

The chart opposite shows how you can help children to develop their ideas from starting points which have given rise to different ideas.

The centre rectangle contains a starter question.

The surrounding 'thought bubbles' contain the sorts of ideas expressed by children.

The further ring of rectangles contains questions posed by teachers in response to the ideas expressed by the children. These questions are meant to prompt children to think about their ideas.

The outer ovals indicate ways in which the children might respond to the teacher's questions.

Some of the shapes have been left blank, as a sign that other ideas may be encountered and other ways of helping children to develop their ideas may be tried.

1 Digestion

As an introduction to developing their ideas about digestion, the children could be given paper cutouts of parts of the digestive system and asked to try to arrange them in their proper places. The copiable sheet on page 68 may be useful here.

The children could be asked:

DIGESTION TAKES PLACE AS THE FOOD TRAVELS FROM THE MOUTH TO THE ANUS

Q *Why do we have all these different parts to the digestive system?*
What do they all do?
What do you think happens to the food as it goes through your body?
What do you think happens to the parts of the food and drink which your body does not need?
What connection is there between what you eat and going to the toilet?
Where in the digestive system is the stomach?
Do you think that food and drink go to the same places?

When the children have had plenty of time to explore their own ideas about digestion, and to exchange some of these ideas with others, they could refer to secondary sources to find out some of the answers to their own questions or to check on the knowledge they already have. Books should be chosen with care – many will have too much information, which could be confusing.

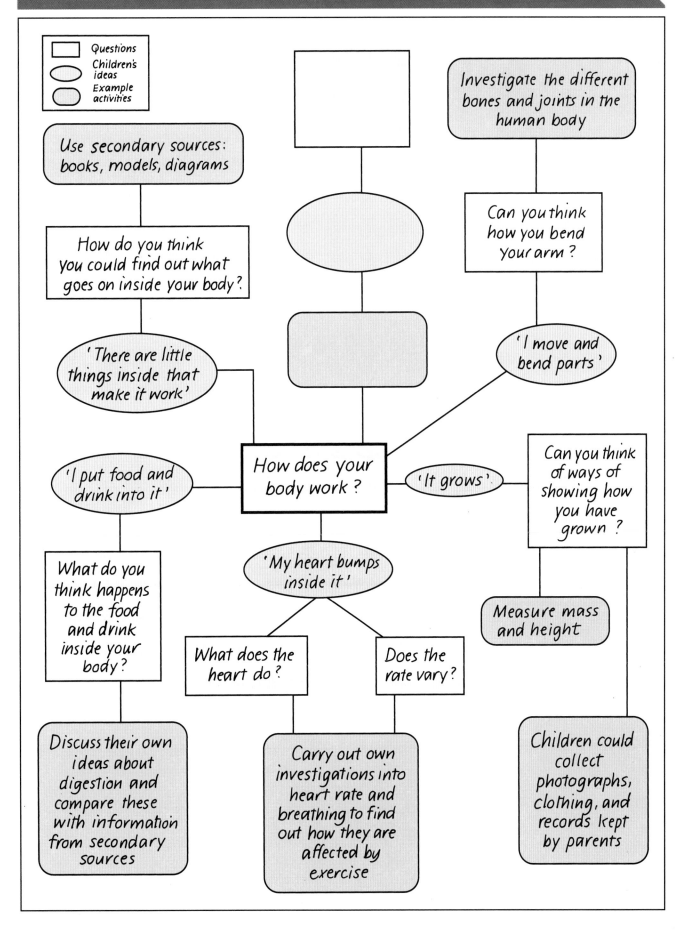

Questions

Children's ideas

Example activities

Use secondary sources: books, models, diagrams

How do you think you could find out what goes on inside your body?

'There are little things inside that make it work'

'I put food and drink into it'

What do you think happens to the food and drink inside your body?

Discuss their own ideas about digestion and compare these with information from secondary sources

How does your body work?

'My heart bumps inside it'

What does the heart do?

Does the rate vary?

Carry out own investigations into heart rate and breathing to find out how they are affected by exercise

Investigate the different bones and joints in the human body

Can you think how you bend your arm?

'I move and bend parts'

'It grows'.

Can you think of ways of showing how you have grown?

Measure mass and height

Children could collect photographs, clothing, and records kept by parents

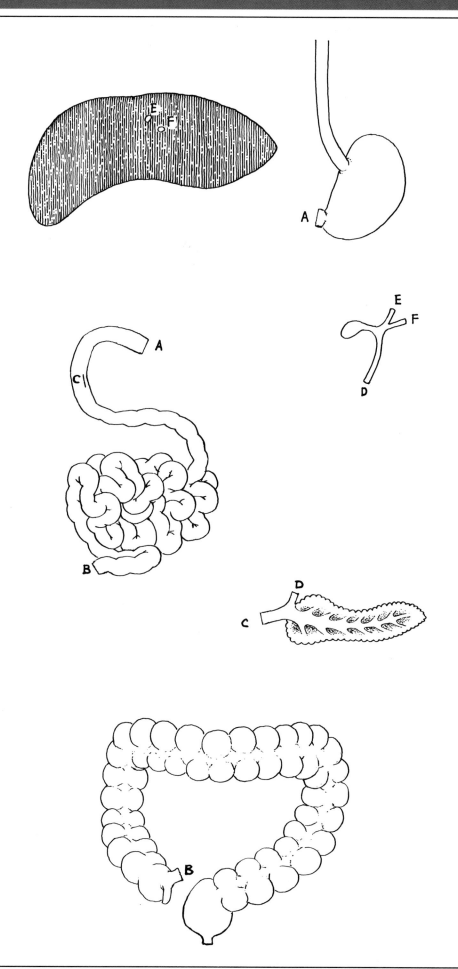

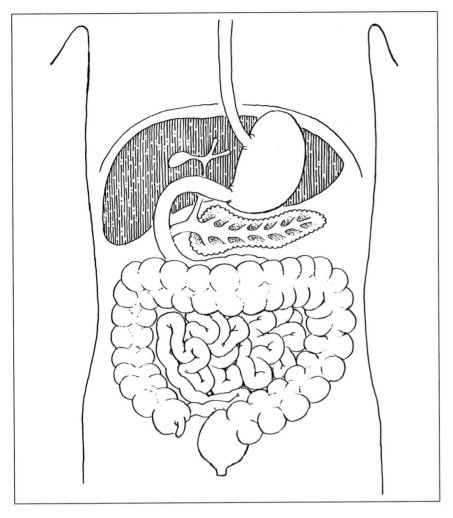

Information about digestion can be found in *Living things in action*.

Other ways of using secondary sources might include:

◆ Children being asked to read a carefully selected passage with understanding, so that they are able to answer some specific questions at the end.
◆ Giving children a passage with missing words and asking them to complete it.
◆ Entering a suitable passage into a computer using a program in which the passage is revealed as children type in certain words correctly.

When the children have found out some information about digestion, one very good way to share the knowledge among the whole class is to dramatize it, for example as 'The story of a piece of toast on its way through the body'. Everyone would take a part, showing what happens to the food as it passes along the alimentary canal.

2 Breathing and circulation

A useful introduction to this work is to ask children for suggestions as to how they could find out more about breathing and circulation. Some of the following ideas may be helpful.

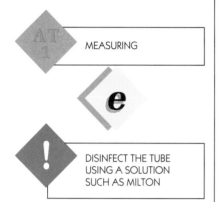

a Chest expansion

Ask the children for their ideas for measuring the amount of air which they breathe in. Here some suggestions.

Children could measure their chest after breathing out and then in, using either a tape measure or simply a piece of string which they could mark.

Blowing up a balloon is a simple way of showing how much air the lungs hold. Make sure that the balloons have already been blown up once (using a balloon pump, not by mouth) so that they are easy to inflate, and don't allow the children to share balloons.

By blowing down a tube and displacing the water in a large upturned jar or bottle, the children will be able to see how much water is displaced by the air in their lungs, thus showing their lung capacity. If you use a bottle as shown in the picture, you can fill it, put the top on, turn it upside-down and take the top off under the water in the sink. (Don't let them over-exert themselves or let it become too competitive.)

Children could be asked:

What do you think your lungs look like?
How does the air get into your lungs?

They could discuss their ideas and show them in a drawing.

Children may have noticed condensation when they breathe on to a cold surface. Ask the children to breathe on to the outside of a beaker filled with cold water, or a window on a cold day, and to think of their own explanation of why this happens.

 Where does the water come from?
What kind of surfaces do you see condensation on?

More about living things in action provides information about breathing.

INTERPRETING
RESULTS AND FINDINGS

b Breathing rate

Get one child to observe another and note how many times she or he breathes during 30 seconds. To start, this should be done when the child being measured is at rest.

The children can double this figure to find the number of breaths per minute.

Ask them to predict what they think will happen to their breathing rate during exercise. Will it stay the same, slow down or get faster? Get the children to devise a fair test to find out how much their breathing alters during and after exercise.

This can be achieved by getting children to run a given distance or to exercise for a set amount of time, measuring their breathing rate before and after.

Children will need a clock or watch that records seconds.

The children could be asked:

 Why do you think we need more air when we exercise?
What do you notice happening to your body when you exercise?
What do you think happens inside you to make your face red when you exercise?
What happens to your heartbeat when you exercise?

c The heart and the circulation

The activity suggested above could be a good starting point for developing ideas about the heart. Some other questions the children could be asked are as follows:

 How do you think the heart works?
What does the heart do?
What do you think the heart is like?

Children could find out about other pumps and how these work. They could also try to make their own pumps, so that they can make a simple 'model heart'.

MEASURING

PLANNING AND
CARRYING OUT FAIR
TESTS

e

t BREATHING RATE
INCREASES DURING
EXERCISE BECAUSE THE
BODY NEEDS MORE
OXYGEN; THE HEART
SPEEDS UP TO DELIVER
MORE BLOOD, WHICH
CARRIES OXYGEN
AROUND THE BODY

 t THE HEART IS A LARGE
MUSCLE THAT PUMPS
BLOOD CONTINUOUSLY
AROUND THE BODY

 e

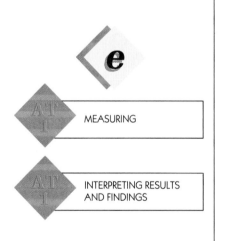

A simple model heart

It is often difficult for children to feel their pulse, especially at their wrist. They may have more success by feeling the pulse in their neck, just below the jaw bone. You may need to explain that their pulse rate is the same as their heart rate – and that both are different from their breathing rate.

Alternatively, children can use a stethoscope to listen to their heartbeat.

They can compare their heartbeat when resting with the rate after exercising. Ask the children to think why their hearts need to beat faster after exercise.

Q *How do you think heart rate is connected to breathing rate?*

Why do both go up after exercise?

Perhaps an adult at the school who is a blood donor would be willing to let the children ask questions about what happens when donating blood.

Children could compile a list of their own questions about breathing and circulation to ask the health visitor or school nurse. They could use secondary sources, such as *More about living things in action*, to find answers to their questions.

Information about the main organs of the body can be found in *More about living things in action*.

MEASURING

INTERPRETING RESULTS AND FINDINGS

! ON NO ACCOUNT SHOULD THERE BE ANY ATTEMPT TO TAKE BLOOD SAMPLES FROM CHILDREN OR ADULTS

pb

3 Bones, muscles and support

a Bending the body

Ask the children for their ideas for investigating how they move.

Here are some suggestions for activities:

Children's awareness of the bones and muscles in their bodies can be developed during PE lessons. As children bend their bodies into different shapes, get them to think about how this is possible, what it is that is actually moving, how it is that they can bend and stretch their bodies.

Ask the children to feel the bones in their bodies. Which of these are they able to name? (Use names such as hip bone and kneecap.) They could do this with a friend, sharing their ideas at the same time.

 OBSERVING

Get the children to find the places where their bodies bend.

 How many joints (bendy places) can you find?
Do you think that all of the joints are the same? Do they all allow you to move in the same way?

Children could compare their own range of movements with that of other children in the class.

 Who can move all their toes?
How far back do your fingers go when you stretch them?
Who can touch the back of their head with their feet when they lie on their stomach?

Many children will at some time have had an injury for which an X-ray picture had to be taken, and may be willing talk about their experience at a hospital. You may be able to obtain some unwanted X-ray photographs from the local hospital.

 COMMUNICATING

b Looking at body movement in more detail

To start their study of movement, children could examine one type of movement in detail, for example running.

Get one of the children to 'run' in slow motion.

 THERE ARE THREE MAIN TYPES OF JOINT: HINGE JOINT (FOR EXAMPLE, THE ELBOW), BALL AND SOCKET JOINT (WHERE THE ARM JOINS THE SHOULDER), AND FLAT JOINT (AS IN THE BACKBONE OR WRIST)

 What kind of body movements do you make when you run?
How are you able to make these movements?
Which parts of the body are used?
Which bones are used when you run?
Which joints do you use when you run?
What kind of joints are these?

 OBSERVING

A model skeleton will give an opportunity for careful observation of the different bones and joints in the human skeleton. The children can discover how many different types of joints there are, and the type of movement afforded by each one.

In addition, well boiled, cleaned and disinfected bones, perhaps from chicken carcasses, could be examined closely with a hand lens.

Videos showing different animal skeletons are useful for making comparisons between different skeletons and their range of movement. Some of the science education programmes on television contain useful sequences. There are also some photographs in *Living things in action*.

The children could use coloured rectangles and squares to make a series of pictures showing the stages in running, using the style shown here.

Children could illustrate body movements by making their own flick books to show someone running, jumping, performing a somersault and so on. They could start by looking at the series of pictures in *Living things in action*.

Ask them to consider different movements, such as picking up an object with the hand or bending the knee. They should think carefully about the movement and the parts of the hand and arm which it involves.

Children could make a model to demonstrate how a hand or a hip joint works. Equipment for this might include elastic bands, springs, straws, pieces of wood, tubing, clay, string, etc.

During a PE lesson, the children could exercise each muscle group separately so that they become aware of the different muscles in their body.

The children could make a model 'arm' from elastic bands and card, showing how the muscles expand and contract as the arm is bent and stretched.

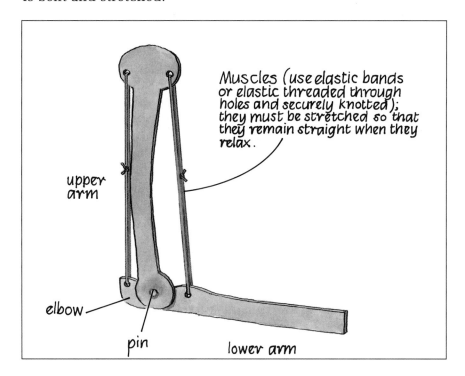

Muscles (use elastic bands or elastic threaded through holes and securely knotted); they must be stretched so that they remain straight when they relax.

upper arm

elbow

pin   lower arm

Living things in action gives further information.

c Parts of the body and their functions

As children carry out their investigations into the human body, they could compare their starting ideas with the ideas they develop during their investigations by completing a chart with headings similar to those shown below.

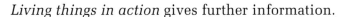

Part of the body	What I think it does	What I hope to find out	What I think about this now

4 Growth and reproduction

If you do not wish to deal with sex education at this point, the children could look at human growth. This section does not deal with sex education in a comprehensive way, as that is outside the scope of this book, but suggests an approach that could be used in conjunction with some of the excellent audio-visual packages which are available. There is no material on sex education in the pupils' books.

SCHOOL SEX EDUCATION POLICY

a Reproduction

You could ask the children:

 Where do you think living things come from?
Where do you think babies grow before they are born?
What has to happen so that a baby starts growing in the first place?
What does the mother do to start a baby?
What does the father do to start a baby?

When talking about human reproduction it is important to establish a common vocabulary with the children. Rather than just giving children the correct scientific terminology, you will need to establish with them which scientific words correspond with the words they commonly use. It is particularly important to do this before showing them books or videos on the subject.

In addition, there are likely to be parts of the human reproductive system with which children may be unfamiliar, such as sperm, ovum, womb and so on.

Human reproduction is usually a fruitful area for children's questions.

Rather than merely answering questions as they arise, it may be helpful to ask the children to compile a list of all their own questions at the outset of this work. In this way the queries can be dealt with in a more logical order, and the children will have a clearer idea of what they hope to find out.

b Growth

The children could be asked some of the following questions:

 How do you know that you have grown since you were a baby?
Do you think that you will stop growing one day?
What is a grown-up, or an adult?
Can you think of ways of showing how you have grown?

Children could think of ways of collecting evidence to show that they have grown. This may include photographs, clothing, records kept by their parents and so on. They could collect data on their growth by keeping a record of such things as shoe and clothing size, height and weight over three months. If any of the children are particularly large or small you may need to handle this sensitively.

Children could talk to their parents, carers, or teachers to collect this information.

Also ask:

 What things can you do now that you were not able to do when you were younger?
Can you think why different people grow at different rates?

c Other animals

Do other animals grow in the same way as people?
How do people change as they grow older?
How do other animals change as they grow into adults?

Children could bring in photographs of their pets to show how they have changed.

They could also consider other animals, including invertebrates, for which they could follow the life cycles through as they change from eggs into adults.

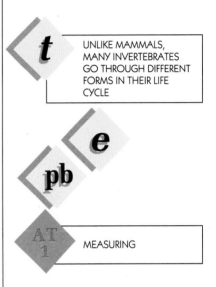

UNLIKE MAMMALS, MANY INVERTEBRATES GO THROUGH DIFFERENT FORMS IN THEIR LIFE CYCLE

Butterfly or moth eggs can be obtained fairly easily and complete their life cycles in a few months.

See *More about living things in action* for information about insect life cycles.

It is easy to keep stick insects in the classroom and to measure their growth. They require a diet of privet leaves kept in a shallow pot of water, which they cannot fall into.

AT 1 MEASURING

Children could record their observations in a log book.

Activities relating to the senses have not been included here but can be found in the *Light*, *Sound and music*, and *Materials* teachers' guides.

Living things in action and *More about living things in action* provide some interesting information about animals.

Living things in action, *Light*, and *More about sound and music* give further information about human and animal senses.

Plants

- The parts of a flowering plant.
- The function of parts of a plant.
- The stages of reproduction in flowering plants.

KEY IDEAS

- Plants form one group of living things. This group includes both flowering plants and non-flowering plants.
- Plants need light, water, carbon dioxide, oxygen and nutrients to grow.
- *Plants can make food from water and carbon dioxide in the presence of light and chlorophyll. This process is called photosynthesis.

(*The asterisk indicates ideas which will be developed more fully in later key stages.)

A LOOK AT plants

In common with all living things, plants respire, excrete, grow, reproduce, sense their surroundings, and require food.

Unlike animals, plants manufacture their own food by photosynthesis. This process takes place in the green parts of a plant, mainly the leaves, and requires carbon dioxide, water and light.

Soil provides nutrients for plants: nitrogen, phosphorus, potassium and smaller amounts of other elements, in various compounds. Adding extra nutrients in the form of fertilizers enriches soil. Plants which do not grow in soil obtain nutrients dissolved in water.

The most common form of plant reproduction is sexual, that is, it requires a male and female part from either the same or a different plant to come together. In a flowering plant male pollen is transferred to the female stigma, and travels down to the ovary. The result of this will be the formation of seeds or fruit. Coniferous plants also have pollen, but their reproductive structures are simpler.

There are various methods of seed dispersal: by the wind, from pods popping open, by sticking to animals. Seeds from inside a fruit may be eaten by an animal and then dispersed when passed out in faeces.

(See also *Variety of life* and *Living things in their environment*.)

Finding out children's ideas

◼ STARTER ACTIVITIES

1 What are plants?

Children may not think of trees, bushes or grass as plants. Take the children to a local park or into the school grounds to look at plants such as annuals, bushes and trees. To find whether they think of all of these as part of the group 'plants', ask:

 Which of these do you think are plants?
Which of these are living?

To find children's criteria for deciding whether plants are alive, ask them to think of their reasons for saying that any plant is or is not living.

 Do you think this plant is living?
Why you think it is living/not living?

Other questions about whether plants are alive or not could also be asked at this stage (see 'How do we know if it is alive?', page 28).

You could give the children a copy of the drawing of a flowering plant on page 81 to see if they are able to name the parts of the plant.

Alternatively, give the children an uprooted common weed to see if they are able to name the main parts.

Next, you could ask them to say what functions they think the various parts of a plant have.

 Why do you think a plant has roots?
Why do you think a plant has flowers?
What happens when the plant dies?
Where do you think the seeds/fruit grow?
What will happen to the seeds/fruit?
What do you think is inside the seeds/fruit?

2 Plant growth

Finding out about plant growth may also be an opportunity for discoveries about other processes of life displayed by plants.

 How could we find out how much plants grow?
What do you think plants need for them to grow?
Draw a plant in a place you think it will grow well.

Leave this enquiry as open as possible so that the children can draw on their experience of familiar plants, indoor or outdoor.

t | PLANTS EXHIBIT THE SAME LIFE PROCESSES AS ANIMALS

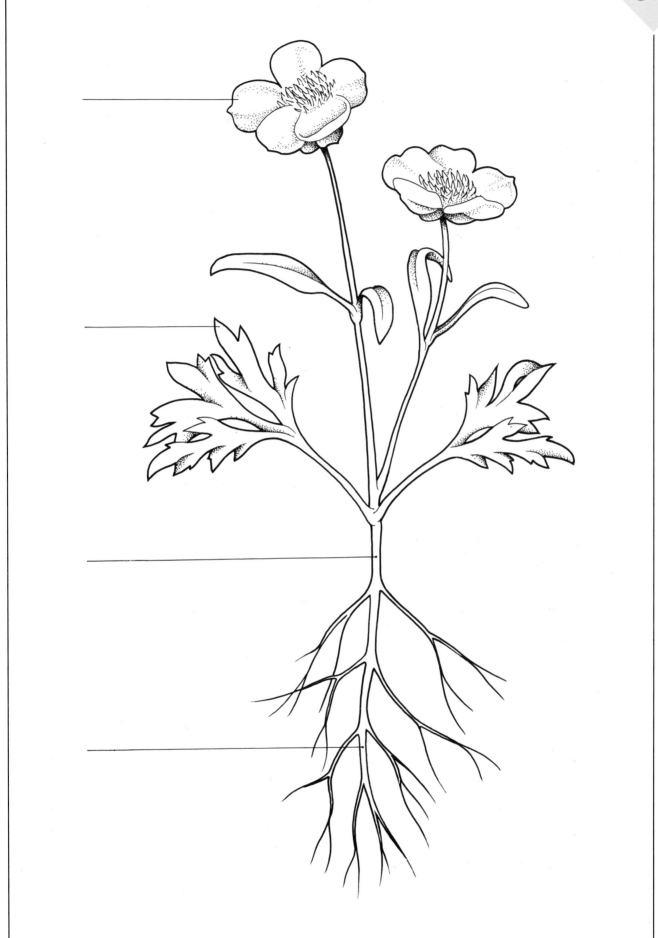

Children's ideas

1 Ideas about plants

Even a word as plain as 'plant' can have a different meaning for teacher and child. A child may not use the word in a biological sense, encompassing a broad range of different plants such as wild flowers, grass, trees, bushes, house plants, and so on, but may use it in a restricted sense to refer to pot plants or to plants which have flowers.

Children are clearly aware of the growth of plants, but seemingly much less so of the other life processes, especially plants' ability to manufacture their own food by using energy from the Sun. They need to have some knowledge of this if they are to understand food chains and the interdependence of organisms.

It is difficult for children at Key Stage 2 to make broad generalizations such as 'Living things all ...' or 'If plants and animals are living things, they all ...'.

The idea that members of a group have common properties is difficult for children to comprehend fully. We can help children develop an understanding of these difficult but essential scientific ideas by continually broadening their experiences so they have more evidence available. This will help them to see patterns emerge as they gather evidence for themselves.

2 Ideas about plant growth

As children progress through Key Stage 2 they increasingly discriminate between light and heat in their description of conditions for plant growth. Some children may mention light sources other than the Sun. The number of conditions increases with the age of the child, the most commonly mentioned being water, soil, Sun, light, and warmth.

Children at Key Stage 2 are more likely to depict plants indoors than younger children. As a result, some children may mention plant food and adequate drainage as important.

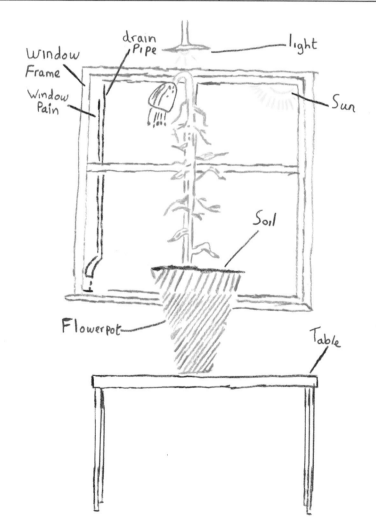

I think the plant needs a lot of light because if it didn't the leaves would shrivel up and it would hang over the table.

The plant will need leaves to get air. It will need roots to collect food and water from the soil and a stem to carry the food to the flower.

Some children may be aware of the nutrient value of the soil in providing food for the plant.

A few children may understand plant growth as a process of incorporation of material from outside the plant. Those children may indicate that parts of the plant, such as the leaves, are formed when nutrients and other materials are incorporated into the plant.

Teacher	*Where do you think the leaves have come from?*
Child	*From the soil, from water, from the air outside, that's it?*

Helping children to develop their ideas

The chart opposite shows how you can help children to develop their ideas from starting points which have given rise to different ideas.

The centre rectangles contain starter questions.

The surrounding 'thought bubbles' contain the sorts of ideas expressed by children.

The further ring of rectangles contains questions posed by teachers in response to the ideas expressed by the children. These questions are meant to prompt children to think about their ideas.

The outer ovals indicate ways in which the children might respond to the teacher's questions.

Some of the shapes have been left blank, as a sign that other ideas may be encountered and other ways of helping children to develop their ideas may be tried.

1 Getting to know plants

a Looking at parts of a plant

Give the children a varied assortment of parts of several plants, such as leaves, flowers, seeds and roots. Avoid poisonous seeds or plants (see *Be safe!* section 12), and seeds which are dressed with pesticides.

Get the children to observe these parts of the plant closely and to say where they think each came from and what function it serves.

 Where do these grow?
What does each one do for the plant?

Carefully uproot a common plant such as a dandelion and wash the soil off the roots.

Get the children to make careful observations of the parts of the plant. Ask them what they think the various parts are for.

 What do you think the roots are for?
Why does a plant have flowers?
Why does a plant have a stem?
Why do plants have seeds/fruits?

More information about seeds can be found in *Living things in action.*

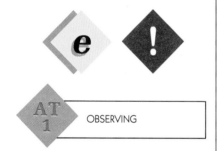

AT 1   OBSERVING

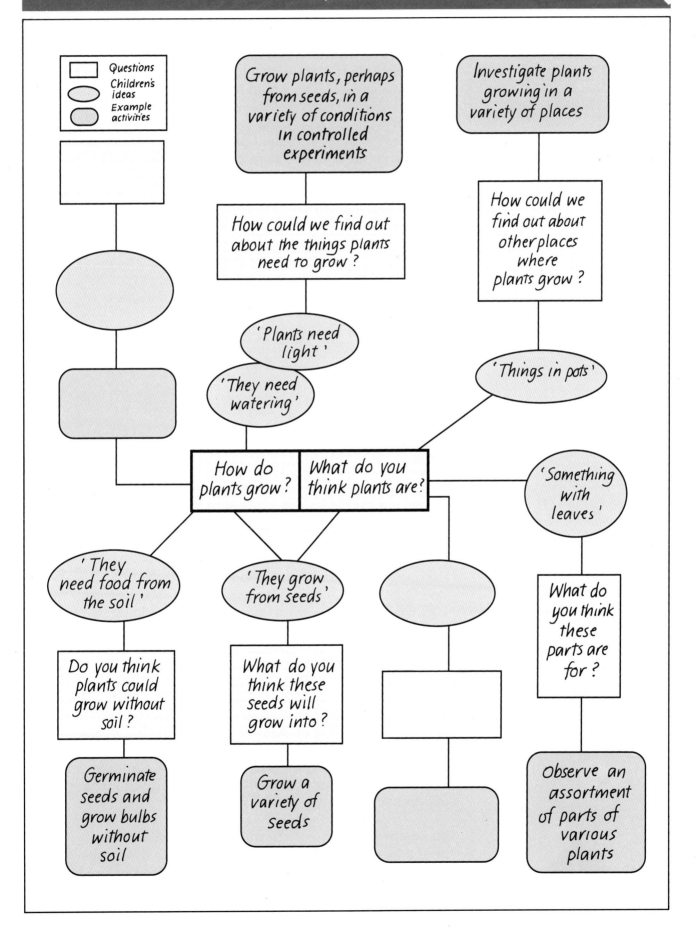

Legend:
- Questions
- Children's ideas
- Example activities

Grow plants, perhaps from seeds, in a variety of conditions in controlled experiments

Investigate plants growing in a variety of places

How could we find out about the things plants need to grow?

How could we find out about other places where plants grow?

'Plants need light'

'They need watering'

'Things in pots'

How do plants grow? | What do you think plants are?

'Something with leaves'

'They need food from the soil'

'They grow from seeds'

What do you think these parts are for?

Do you think plants could grow without soil?

What do you think these seeds will grow into?

Germinate seeds and grow bulbs without soil

Grow a variety of seeds

Observe an assortment of parts of various plants

85

OBSERVING
MEASURING

b Observing plants

Children could find a plant in the school grounds and make regular observations of it throughout its life cycle. For this purpose it is better to select a common weed such as a thistle, dandelion, daisy or hawkweed, as these plants are likely to have fairly short life cycles in the growing season. Children could mark their plant with a lollipop stick so that they can identify it easily. If the school has a wildlife area, this will be an ideal place to carry out these investigations. If it does not, why not establish one? Even an area as small as one metre square can provide sufficient plants to study. Alternatively, the children could establish a growing area in an old bath or sink, or sections of sewer pipes – these large concrete pipes make excellent plant tubs when stood on end on tarmac or concrete, and are fairly cheap.

Children can keep a book to chart the life of their plant under a title such as 'Three months in the life of a ...' They may not speculate about why their plants flourishes or dies back at certain times; if so, prompt them to suggest reasons.

Children could use *Living things in action* to find out about how we use parts of plants for cooking.

2 Plant growth

 Do plants need light? warmth? soil?

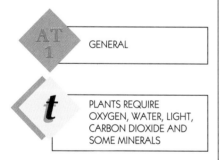
GENERAL

PLANTS REQUIRE
OXYGEN, WATER, LIGHT,
CARBON DIOXIDE AND
SOME MINERALS

Children could investigate their ideas about the conditions required for plant growth. They will need to look at ways of devising a fair test so that they can isolate one factor.

For example, if children are trying to find out whether plants will grow in the dark, they will need to carry out a separate investigation to find out if they can grow without water. You may wish to discuss all the possible ways of doing this first, so that children carry out a range of investigations between them.

For growing plants, it is a good idea to choose an appropriate time of the year for plant growth – that is, spring or summer. If this is not possible, children should use plants that will grow at any time of the year, such as mung beans, cress seeds, wheat or rice. In the spring or summer, suitable seeds for germinating are any cereals such as wheat, barley, oats, rice, or broad beans. These grow readily and are easy to measure. Children could also try growing bulbs. (Avoid white hyacinths, to which some children are allergic.)

Make sure that the seeds have not been treated with a pesticide, as this could make handling them dangerous. Most commercial seeds will have been treated – it would be best to get them from a health food shop.

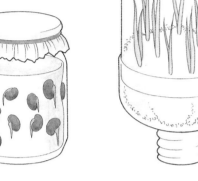

mung beans

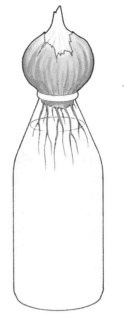

wheat seedlings

onion

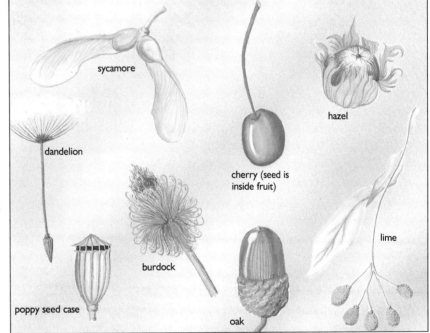

sycamore

dandelion

poppy seed case

burdock

cherry (seed is inside fruit)

hazel

oak

lime

Children may like to germinate seeds they have collected directly from plants. Some seeds can be planted at once, but others (such as annuals native to Britain) may need to be overwintered in a refrigerator or freezer for a few weeks, or left until the following spring.

At the outset of their investigations, ask the children to predict what the seeds will grow into.

Do they realize that wheat seeds only grow into wheat plants or that carrot seeds only grow into carrot plants – that is, that living things reproduce their own kind?

You could ask the children some of the following:

 What do you think your seeds will need to help them to grow?
What is inside the seed?
What will start your seed growing?

Annotated drawings are a useful way of finding out children's ideas about seeds.

When growing their seeds, children could keep a log book to chart their progress, measuring the height of the plant, noting the root growth and any other observations.

Get the children to think about other life processes in plants by

AT 1   MEASURING

 OBSERVING

asking them:

 Do you think plants breathe? feed? move? etc.

Discussion ideas about the needs of plants can be found in *More about living things in action.*

Can flowers move?

The children could place some flowering plants in a position where there is only one light source.

After a day, ask the children to observe which way the flowers are pointing, then turn the flower round and look next day to see what has happened.

PLANTS MOVE IN
RESPONSE TO LIGHT

Others flowers which open and close can also be observed, for example daisy, mesembrianthemum or maranta (prayer plant).

 Why do you think the plants/flowers move?
Do plants move in the same way as animals move?

See *More about living things in action.*

You may wish to relate this work on plant responses to the position of the Sun to activities in *The Earth in Space* (see the teachers' guide, page 52).

CHAPTER 4 Assessment

4.1 Introduction

You will have been assessing your children's ideas and skills by using the activities in this teachers' guide. This on-going, formative assessment is essentially part of teaching since what you find is immediately used in suggesting the next steps to help the children's progress. But this information can also be brought together and summarized for purposes of recording and reporting progress. This summary of performance has to be in terms of National Curriculum level descriptions at the end of the key stages, and some schools keep records in terms of levels at other times.

This chapter helps you summarize the information you have from children's work in terms of level descriptions. Examples of work relating to the theme of this guide are discussed and features which indicate activity at a certain level are pointed out to show what to look for in your pupils' work as evidence of achievement at one level or another. It is necessary, however, to look across the full range of work, and not judge from any single event or piece of work.

There are two sets of examples provided. The first is the assessment of skills in the context of the activities related to the concepts covered in this guide. The second deals with the development of these concepts.

4.2 Assessment of skills (AT1)

Things to look for when pupils are investigating living processes as indicating progress from level 2 to level 5:

Level 2: Making suggestions as well as responding to others' suggestions about how to find things out about living things. Using equipment and living things suitably housed and cared for, to make observations. Recording what they find and comparing it with what they expected.

Level 3: Saying what they expect to happen when something is changed and suggesting ways of collecting information to test their predictions. Carrying out fair tests, knowing why they are fair, and making measurements. Recording what they find in a variety of ways; noticing any patterns in it.

Level 4: Making predictions which guide the planning of fair tests. Using suitable equipment and making adequate and relevant observations. Using tables and charts to record measurements and other observations. Interpreting, drawing conclusions and attempting to relate findings to scientific knowledge.

Level 5: Planning controlled investigations of predictions which are based on scientific knowledge. Using equipment carefully, repeating observations as necessary. Using line graphs to record and help interpretation; considering findings in relation to scientific knowledge.

Sarah, Suzanne, Christopher and John were challenged by their teacher to think about how the blood is moved round the body.

The children discussed their ideas and began pressing a hand against the chest to feel their own heart beating.

The teacher asked if they knew of any other way of finding their heart beat. John suggested taking the pulse at the wrist and the teacher showed how to find the pulse in the neck. The children began counting the beats. The teacher asked:

How many times will your heart beat in one minute?

After making a prediction, the children used a timer to count their heart beats. John put the results in a table.

When the children compared the counts they were surprised by Sarah's low heart beat. Sarah was the smallest in the group.

John	63 beats
Sarah	50 beats
Suzanna	65 beats
Chris	65 beats
Sir	71 beats

John

The children suggested that the heart beat increased with the person's size. They decided to take the teacher's pulse to find out if they were correct. They predicted that the teacher's heart beat would be higher than any of their heart beats. Christopher, John and Sarah wrote their predictions down and Christopher described why he thought the teacher's count would be high.

The children also discussed whether an adult's heart beat could be different for other reasons, such as age.

After taking the teacher's pulse the children suggested that an adult's heart beat was higher because of age and size.

The teacher asked:

How can you find out how people's size affects their heart beat?

Christopher

Find out how our heart beat changes
I think it will beat 67 in a min.
I Found out that my heart beats 65 times
doese adults hearts beat Faster or slower
Then childrens heats.
I think sirs heart beats 89 times because the
blood takes longer to travle around the body.
We found that it was 71 times minute.

find out how are hart beat changes

I think it will beat 65 times in one minute
but it lasted 50 times

are adults hearts faster than children

I think they are faster

67 in a minute

The real anwser was 71 sec

Sarah

find out How are heart beat changes ♡

We measured our pulse with a stop clock

Mine	65 per min	These Were Our results
Sirs	71 per min	
Chriskoper	65 per min	
Johns	63 per min	
Sarahs	50 per min	

Suzanna

Find out how our heart beat changes

I think it will beat 60 times a min.

I found out that my heart beats

63 times a minute.

We are going find out if older
peoples heart beats are faster
or slower.

I think Sirs heart will beat

80 times a minute.

We found that Sirs heart beats

71 times a minute.

John

The children decided that they could find out about size from measuring height and weight. They chose to measure using a metre stick and bathroom scales.

John

We are going to weigh and measure each other and see if height make a difference.

Name	Height	Weight	
John	1 4 7	7¼ st	
Sarah	1 2 9	4 st	
Suzanna	1 3 4	5½ st	
Chris	1 4 7	7 st	
Sir	1 7 1	11½	

I think that height and weight have nothing do with it because Chris and Suzanna have the same heart beat but they're not the same height or weight.

Suzanna

We thought it was our weight and height that might change our heart beat.

Mine	5 st ½	Weight
Sirs	11 ½	
Sarahs	3 st ½	
John	7 st 3 pounds	
chris	7 st	

Mine	134	height
Sirs	171	
Sarahs	129	
John	147	
Chris	147	

We found out that height and Weight dos'nt matter as me and chris had the same pulse

Christopher

we going to measure and weigh each other
to see if height makes a diffrerence.

	height Estimate	Answer		weight Esimate	Answer
John	15.3	147	Jhon	6 stone	7 Stone 3 pou
Sarah	120	129	sarah	4 Stone	4 sfone
Suzanna	140	134	SUZanna	5 Stone	5½ stone
Chris	150	147	Sir	9 Stone	11½
Sir	195	171	chris	6½ stone	7 Stone

we Found out that height and weight dosn't matter

we are going to measure and weigh each other
to see if height or weight makes a diffrence

Suzannas height 121 anwser 134
christopher height 150 anwser 147
John height 141 anwser 147
sarah height 112 anwser 129
Sir height 198 anwser 171
Suzannas weight 5 and a half anwser 5 and a half
christophers weight 6 hale anwser 7 stone
John weight 4 anwser 7 quarter
sarah weight 4 anwser 4
Sir weight 12 anwser 11 and a half

we have found out that height and weight does not matter

Sarah

The children all made predictions and Christopher provided a reason
for his prediction of the teacher's heart beat, based on knowledge of
what the heart does. They all compared what they found with what
they had expected.

Having found a difference among their pulse rates they decided to investigate possible reasons for the differences, refining the idea of 'size' into height and weight. They planned and carried out their investigation, measuring weight and height with appropriate instruments. They all tabulated their findings, but the results in John's table are far more easy to understand than in Sarah's and Suzanne's. Christopher recorded estimates as well as measured heights and weights, although no comments are made about the accuracy of these estimates. They were interestingly close to the measurements, however, indicating a good feel for the units involved.

From their results, helped by their definition and quantification of 'size', the children were able to conclude that their original idea was incorrect. They justified this conclusion by noting that two children had the same pulse rate but different heights and weights. Although not looking across the results for patterns, they linked their conclusions to the original question.

There are many indications here of work at level 3 and of progress towards level 4, particularly in Christopher, who used scientific knowledge in his prediction. There are several opportunities for extension of, or reflection on, this investigation, which would help the children to develop their investigation skills further. They could be asked, for example:

> *What made you think that the heart beat changed with size?*
> *How could you find out if the counts in the your group are typical of children?*
> *How could you find out the range of heart beats we have in the class?*

4.3 Assessment of children's understanding (Part of AT2)

Aspects of work relating to living processes indicating progression from level 2 to level 5:

Level 2: Awareness of the need of living things for food, air and water. Recognizing that living things grow and reproduce.

Level 3: Showing knowledge of the basic life processes and using it to distinguish between living and non-living things.

Level 4: Showing awareness of the organs which support life processes, such as the heart and lungs, and their position in the human body. Identifying petals, stamens and stigma in plants.

Level 5: Explaining the main functions of organs of the human body, such as the heart, lungs and kidneys and of petals, stamens and stigma in plants. Explaining why these are essential in terms of supporting life processes such as nutrition, growth, respiration, and reproduction. Describing the life cycles of plants and animals and some similarities between them.

You need to water planks and
Put baby bio underneath planks
You need to keep planks by the sun
only some planks need to be by the
sun.

Jose

Jose has described how she takes care of a house plant. The conditions she feels are necessary for keeping the plant alive are shown in this description. In Jose's view, it appears that the plant needs water, the Sun and perhaps food (expressed as 'baby bio'). Often children do not express the need for light or the Sun directly, as Jose does. Instead, they show this need by placing the plant near a window, as Jose also indicates. Jose appears to be aware that green plants need light, an indication of work at level 2.

Michael has described how he takes care of his pets. His description suggests he is aware of the conditions necessary for keeping an animal alive. The needs appear to be food, water and warmth. His work is at level 2.

Victoria (overleaf) has been able to describe the needs of both a plant and an animal. In her illustration of the care of her pet, Jazz, she appears to be aware that Jazz needs food. Taken together, these descriptions show her work is at level 2.

We give him food and water,
and a nice warm bed

Michael

We give him food and water
and straw, hay and a nice hutch

This Flower has rain and sun The Flower can spred its roats in the soil.

Victoria

This Flower has't got rain, and sun so it can't spred it's roats in the soil. It needs rain and sun so it can sped it's roats.

Jazzs home

Jazzs water

Jazzs sleeping 15

Jazzs eating pot

Amanda, Senal (shown opposite) and Jody (page 98) have described some of the similarities between how they live, and how their pets live.

Although Amanda ascribes human characteristics to her hamster, she is aware that animals and humans feed and move, and her work appears to be closer to level 3 than to level 2.

Senal's description shows a greater appreciation of the basic processes common to living things. By showing that waste is removed from the bodies of animals and humans, Senal shows a greater awareness of how living organisms function, and perhaps, in her view, is giving a description of the result of the feeding process.

Our Hampster like's eating food like me. Our hampster like's sleeping like me. Our hampster like's running like me. Our Hampster like's climing like me.

Amanda

My fish's eat's food plays games swim's gose to the Toloe. and look's at Me I eat food go to the tolet plag games and swim and I Look at the fish.

Senal

In addition, Senal's drawing shows that she is aware of animals breathing but she has not suggested that humans and animals have this process in common. Although children may be aware of both animals and humans breathing, they may feel that it is too obvious to mention.

Jody, in describing her rabbit, has also omitted breathing as a shared process but she includes the same detail as Senal.

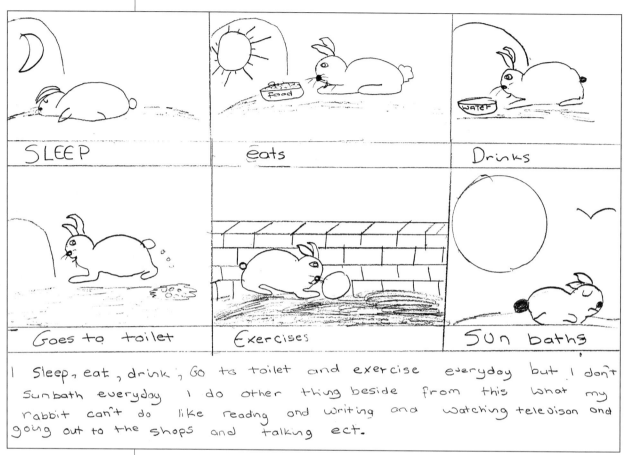

SLEEP	eats	Drinks
Goes to toilet	Exercises	Sun baths

I Sleep, eat, drink, Go to toilet and exercise everyday but I don't sunbath everyday I do other thing beside from this what my rabbit can't do like reading and writing and watching televison and going out to the shops and talking ect.

Jody

The detail offered by Jody and Senal, together with evidence gathered elsewhere on breathing, and possibly reproduction, indicates work at level 3.

In their drawings (shown opposite) James, Lisa and Sharon have shown some parts of the human body which are involved in breathing and nutrition.

James has named some internal parts of the body but he does not seem to be aware of the separate functions of lungs and organs involved in processing food. This work does not meet the requirements for level 4. Lisa's drawing shows greater awareness of the positions of lungs and stomach but her knowledge of the breathing system appears to be limited to the existence of lungs. Both James and Lisa need to develop a greater awareness of the organs which support breathing and feeding for their work to achieve level 4.

Sharon's work is a little more advanced in having identified the separate channels for food and air but her grasp of the location of the organs needs to be clarified in discussion of her drawing.

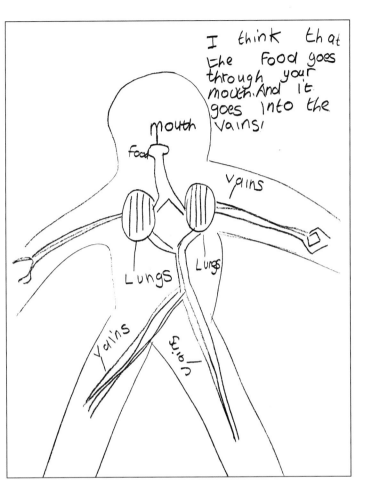

I think that the food goes through your mouth. And it goes into the vains.

mouth
Food
vains
Lungs
Lungs
Yains
vains

James

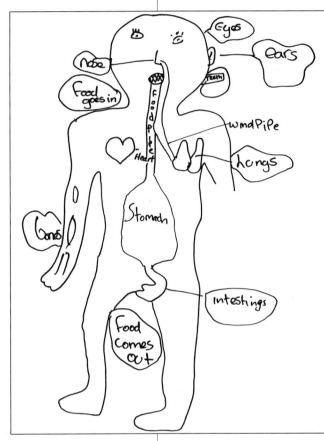

Eyes
Nose
Ears
Teeth
Food goes in
windpipe
Heart
lungs
Bones
Stomach
intestings
Food comes out

Sharon

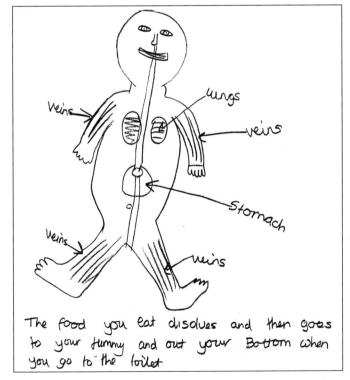

Veins
lungs
veins
stomach
veins
veins

The food you eat disolves and then goes to your tummy and out your Bottom when you go to the toilet

Lisa

99

In addition to the breathing and feeding systems, John has been able to show parts of the circulatory system. He has also been able to connect the circulatory system with digestion and repair of the body. These aspects of John's work are at level 5.

To confirm that he was working at level 5, John would have to provide more detail of the circulatory system and demonstrate an awareness of the function of organ systems in flowering plants.

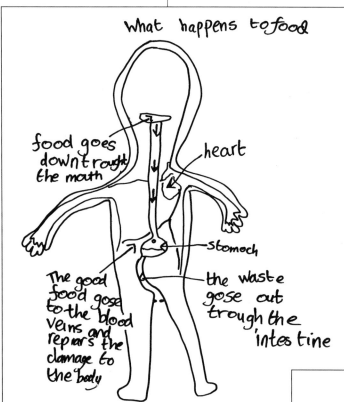

John

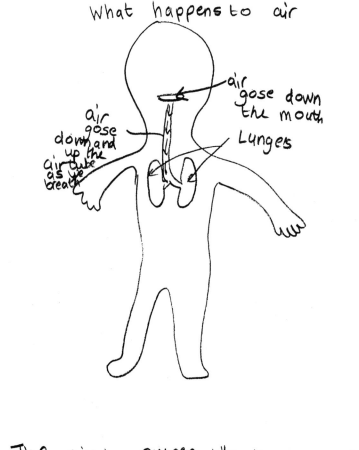

John

CHAPTER 5

Background science

The processes of life

'Processes of life' is a general term used for the characteristics which are common to all living things: they are made of cells, and they can move, respond to stimuli, grow, feed, respire, excrete and reproduce. These processes are used by scientists to decide if an organism (plant or animal) is living.

In scientific terms, an animal is any living organism which feeds on other organisms and moves. That means that a spider, an amoeba and a tiger are all animals. Children, and many adults, tend to use the word 'animal' to refer to what scientists call a mammal. A mammal is any living organism which has lungs, is warm blooded, has hair on its body and usually develops inside its mother.

All organisms have the following properties in common.

1 Growth

Both plants and animals are continually growing, even though this is not always obvious, as in the case of adult animals. All organisms are made of cells in much the same way as a house is made of bricks. The human body, for instance, consists of some one hundred million million cells. Plant and animal cells differ in their structure, but all cells contain a cell membrane, which is a covering for the cell; a nucleus, which contains important genetic information and acts as a control centre; and cytoplasm in which the chemical reactions for making things and releasing energy from food take place.

In both plants and animals, cells are continually being replaced as they die. This growth is brought about by the division of cells to form new ones. The division of cells usually takes place at specific sites in the organism. For example, in humans new blood cells are manufactured by the bone marrow inside the large limb bones, and skin cells are formed under existing skin.

Typical plant cell
Typical animal cell

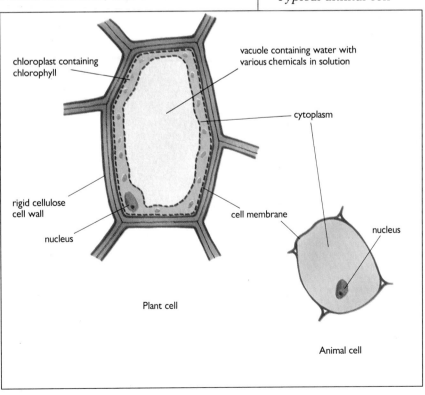

chloroplast containing chlorophyll

vacuole containing water with various chemicals in solution

cytoplasm

rigid cellulose cell wall

cell membrane

nucleus

nucleus

Plant cell

Animal cell

2 Movement

All plants and animals are capable of movement, usually in response to some kind of stimulus. Plants normally move slowly, as a result of growth. Plants' leaves will grow to reach an optimum position for obtaining light; most of us have observed this phenomenon in the case of house plants turning towards the window.

Some plants may grow in a spiral way and twine their tendrils around anything they can find to cling on to.

One plant that can actually be seen to move is the Maranta, or Prayer Plant, whose leaves suddenly point upwards as it gets darker in the evening. Another example is the Venus Fly Trap, which closes its leaves around any insect unfortunate enough to land on it. Plants such as Marram Grass or Bamboo curl their leaves up to prevent them from drying out.

Animals move to find food, to shelter themselves from light, to escape from predators or to find a dry, warm, or damp place. One of the main differences between plant and animal movement is that plants do not move from place to place; they move only one organ in response to a stimulus: the roots grow towards the centre of the earth (**geotropism**) and the leaves grow towards the light (**phototropism**).

Generally, plants do not respond to stimuli as obviously or as quickly as animals.

3 Feeding

In order to grow, a living thing (organism) must take substances into its body. This is done by feeding. Animals and green plants feed in very different ways. The basic difference between green plants and animals is that plants can make their own food but animals cannot.

All life processes require energy. Animals obtain this energy from the food they eat, whereas plants, being capable of manufacturing their own food, utilize energy from the Sun during a process called **photosynthesis** (see page 109).

It is often mistakenly thought that plants get all their food from soil or from plant food. What soil and plant food actually do provide are the essential mineral salts necessary for many of the chemical reactions which take place at a cellular level. However, they are not a source of energy. Plants use a combination of carbon dioxide, water from the soil, energy from the Sun in the form of light, and **chlorophyll** in their leaves to make organic chemicals, mainly sugar, which are their basic food. (It is the chlorophyll in their leaves which makes them green.) Much of the sugar is turned into starch for storage in the leaves.

In all living things, both energy and amino acids – the building blocks of proteins – are essential for the generation of new cells. Energy is mainly provided by the foods known as carbohydrates and fats. The most well known carbohydrates are sugar and starch. Many organisms can store food in some form. For example, the human body can store only a little carbohydrate but can store large amounts of fat.

Animals, both herbivores (plant eaters) and carnivores (animal eaters), are ultimately dependent on plants as a source of protein. Animals can synthesize amino acids from one protein into a different protein, but somewhere in the food chain these proteins came from plant material. For example, hawks eat rabbits for their protein, but rabbits eat grass for theirs.

A typical food chain

Food is needed by plants and animals for growth, as an energy source, and for the replacement of worn or damaged tissues.

4 Respiration

First and foremost, it is very important to appreciate that respiration is not the same thing as breathing. The two are often confused.

Respiration is a chemical reaction between food and oxygen which releases energy. It takes place in the cells of all living things.

Although the process of respiration is a complicated one, it can be simplified as follows. In a complex chemical reaction, food containing carbon, hydrogen and oxygen atoms combines with more oxygen atoms, provided by breathing, to eventually produce carbon dioxide and water and to release energy.

In mammals, the carbon dioxide generated in the process of respiration passes into the blood, which carries it to the lungs. Plants release the carbon dioxide through the pores in their leaves. (See page 110).

Breathing is the process of taking in air, absorbing oxygen from it, and releasing the carbon dioxide into it. Mammals breathe by using their lungs to take in oxygen from air and get rid of carbon dioxide. Fish use their gills for the same purpose, except that the oxygen is dissolved in water rather than being part of the air.

Some organisms, such as yeast, can respire, that is break down complex chemicals (food) and transfer energy without oxygen. This process is called **anaerobic respiration**.

5 Excretion

An organism is a sophisticated machine which takes in a variety of chemicals and then either breaks them down to transfer energy, or builds them up to make structures like muscles and bones. The technical term for this process is **metabolism**.

However, some of the products of this process are poisonous, so they must be removed from the body or they will harm the organism. In humans, the chemical urea and solid wastes must be removed. The process of removing them from the body is called excretion.

Plants remove waste substances in a different way. They turn some of them into harmless substances which they store. Some of them are transferred to the leaves in autumn and then shed from the plant. Some substances are released from all parts of the plant through pores.

6 Reproduction

Organisms produce offspring, and this process is known as reproduction.

Sexual reproduction involves a male and a female of the species. In mammals, the male produces sperm and the female produces eggs. The male and female come into close contact and the male passes the sperm to the female. These unite with the egg to fertilize it. The fertilized egg, which is called an embryo, develops into a new individual.

Some organisms can reproduce on their own without the help of another. This is called asexual reproduction and, in its simplest form, the organism simply splits in two. (Aphids are also capable of asexual reproduction, in which females give birth to daughters.) Plants frequently reproduce by asexual (or vegetative) reproduction – for instance by cuttings (e.g. roses), tubers (e.g. potatoes), runners (e.g. strawberries), or by pieces of root being broken off (e.g. dandelion).

The human body

Digestion

Food is needed both for growth and as a source of energy for the many chemical reactions which take place in the body. The nutrients which the body requires are absorbed from our food as it passes along the alimentary canal (digestive tract).

The digestive tract consists of a long tube stretching from the mouth to the anus. The food passing through it is broken down into smaller particles, both physically and chemically, until it consists of molecules which can pass through the surface of the wall into the blood stream. The chemicals needed for digestion are supplied by the liver, pancreas and digestive glands.

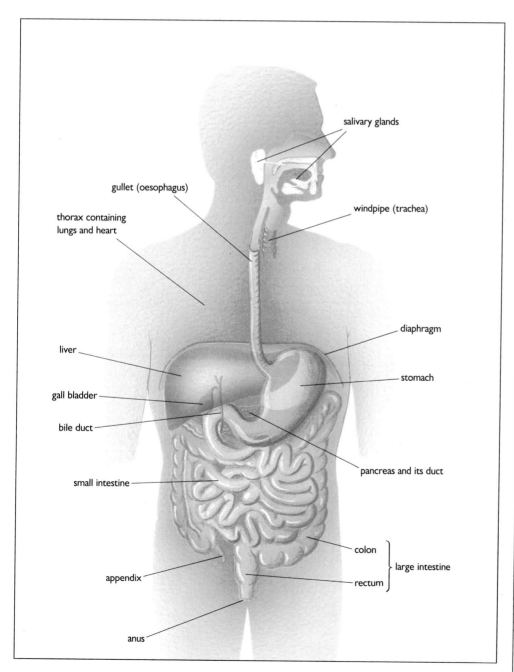

The digestive tract of a human being

The digestive process

1 Food is chewed and broken down into smaller pieces. Saliva helps to lubricate the food as it goes down the oesophagus and into the stomach, where the process of breaking it down begins.

2 In the stomach, digestive juices, including hydrochloric acid, mix with the food and break it down. The muscles of the stomach help in this process.

3 Food passes through a short tube, the duodenum, into the small intestine. Most of the nutrients are absorbed through the walls of the intestine into the blood stream. The small intestine is very long, typically 5 to 6 metres.

4 The food moves on to the large intestine, where water is absorbed and undigested materials are stored as faeces until they are expelled through the anus.

Diet

Many health problems associated with the digestive system are a result of a poor diet. It may contain too much sugar, too little fibre (a result of eating too much processed food) or too many harmful substances such as caffeine, alcohol or fat. The bad effects of poor eating may take many years to manifest themselves, so it is important that children are aware from an early age of the effect of diet on their health. It is important for all of us that we eat a well balanced diet.

At different stages in our lives we have different diet requirements. For example, children and pregnant women need a higher proportion of protein to provide the amino acids essential for building new cells. Hard physical work requires a diet with more carbohydrates to supply energy. Older people need less food in total and in particular need less protein.

In addition to the foods already mentioned, a balanced diet also includes small quantities of vitamins and minerals. In fact, they are normally present in sufficient quantities in an ordinary diet containing vegetables, fats, cereals, and meat or fish. Only people who restrict themselves to a very limited diet, such as vegans who eat no animal products, may need to take supplements to ensure that they have all the essential proteins and vitamins.

The chief concerns about Western diets are the lack of dietary fibre, overeating and the amount of harmful additives contained in the food we eat. Fibre is essential for maintaining a healthy digestive tract. Overeating results in obesity, which places an extra strain on the heart and the arteries and reduces circulation to other parts of the body. Many chemicals are added to flavour, preserve and colour our food. Even fresh fruits such as oranges sometimes have mineral oil added to make them look more appealing. Frequently, we are not even aware of the presence of additives. Until recently, for example, few people realized that sugar is often added to savoury foods such as baked beans, bread and hamburgers. Some additives may be harmful to health, but they do help to preserve food and improve its flavour.

Many of the attitudes we have towards food and eating were developed at an early age. For this reason, health education programmes in schools are needed to provide children with the information they need in order to make informed choices and to establish good eating habits.

Breathing and circulation

The body needs a constant supply of oxygen for the process of respiration in order to stay alive. Oxygen from the air is absorbed by the lungs and transported to all parts of the body by the blood.

The lungs consist of many branching tubes which end in a collection of tiny air sacs, giving it a sponge-like texture. Blood which is depleted in oxygen (deoxygenated blood) is pumped from the heart to the lungs via the pulmonary artery. In the lungs the artery branches into tiny thin-walled tubes called **capillaries**, which surround the tiny sacs of the lungs. In these sacs, oxygen passes through the cell walls and combines with a chemical in the red blood cells (**haemoglobin**) to replenish the blood with oxygen. Blood returning to the lungs has a bluish appearance, whereas the oxygenated blood which flows from the lungs is bright red.

The **arteries**, which take blood from the heart, have muscular walls which, by contracting, help the blood to circulate. The **veins** return blood to the heart, and are not so muscular. In some people the veins do not function efficiently and become engorged with blood, causing varicose veins.

During one circuit of the body the blood goes through the heart twice. Deoxygenated blood passes through the heart on its way to the lungs and then it is returned to the heart, from where it is pumped round the rest of the body, as shown opposite.

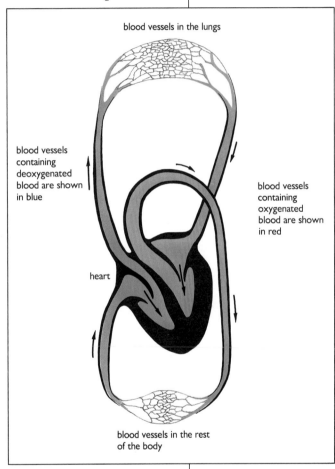

blood vessels in the lungs

blood vessels containing deoxygenated blood are shown in blue

blood vessels containing oxygenated blood are shown in red

heart

blood vessels in the rest of the body

The heart/lung circulation system

The heart

The heart is a large, muscular organ which keeps working throughout our lives, pumping blood through the body. When doctors or nurses feel our pulse, they are measuring the rate at which the heart is pumping. The rate is around 70 beats per minute, but it can vary markedly, depending on the state of the body and the level of activity, or whether it has been placed under sudden stress. The contractions of the heart muscle can be felt as a pulse of blood in an artery at the wrist or in the neck. Children's pulses can be felt more easily in their neck, just below the jaw bone.

The heart is divided into four compartments which contain valves to help keep the blood flowing in one direction. Deoxygenated blood flows through one half of the heart and oxygenated blood flows through the other half – into arteries and around the body.

Keeping our hearts and lungs healthy

The intricate structures of the lungs can be easily damaged by foreign particles such as smoke or dust which clog up the minute passageways and cause irritation; they may lead eventually to diseases such as bronchitis, cancer or emphysema.

The lungs can also be damaged by long-term exposure to polluted air, especially in cities. Haemoglobin in the red blood cells, which normally combines with oxygen, combines more readily with the carbon monoxide given off by car exhausts. The effect is that the supply of oxygen is diminished and the heart has to beat faster to compensate.

Both the heart and the lungs benefit from physical exertion. This needs to be borne in mind especially by people who have sedentary jobs or children who travel to school by car or public transport. This may mean taking up sport or exercise such as walking, running, or cycling. The heart, like other muscles, is more likely to be maintained in a healthy condition by regular exercise, which requires it to work harder than it does for normal body maintenance. In the same way, the lungs do not expand to capacity during inactivity. Regular exercise results in increased efficiency and greater lung capacity.

Movement and support

Muscles, bones and joints provide the body with a structure that is both supportive and allows flexibility of movement. It is not only children who fail to appreciate that muscles pervade the whole body and are needed for every movement that we make!

Every movement is controlled by muscles, of which there are two types:

◆ Voluntary muscles are used for deliberate movements. They come in pairs. For example, you use one set of muscles to bend your arm and another set to straighten it.

◆ Involuntary muscles, such as those which control the heart and the digestive tract, work without any conscious control.

Muscles are made of many filaments which slide over each other when stimulated by a nerve impulse; this action causes them to contract.

The liver

The liver, one of the most important organs in the body, is located just below the diaphragm, overlapping the stomach. It has several functions.

◆ Regulation of blood sugar. After a meal, glucose is passed to the liver which stores what is surplus to the body's immediate requirements.

- Production of bile, which helps in the digestion of fats. People with hepatitis, a disease of the liver, have difficulty digesting fats.

- Iron from old red blood cells which are broken down is stored in the liver and then released with the bile.

- Toxic substances are removed from the blood. The liver frequently becomes diseased if people consume large quantities of alcohol over a long period.

- In addition, the liver makes the protein found in blood plasma, and stores vitamins A and D.

- During these chemical processes, heat is produced and is distributed around the body by the blood.

- Removal of excess proteins. Most people in the West eat too much protein. The liver breaks down proteins and produces urea which is carried by the blood to the kidneys.

The kidneys

The main function of the kidneys is to remove soluble waste products from the blood and to assist in the process of excretion. The process of excretion is the removal from the body of:

- waste products, both solid and liquid, resulting from chemical reactions;
- excess water;
- used-up hormones.

The kidneys are one of the main sites for excretion, although it does also occur in the lungs (carbon dioxide and water), liver (bile), and skin (water and salt in sweat).

The two kidneys are located towards the back of the abdomen. A tube (the ureter) leads from each of them into the bladder. The kidneys themselves consist of a mass of very small tubes. As the blood passes through the tubes under pressure, they filter out unwanted substances and excess liquid. This solution then continues as urine to the bladder where it collects until it is expelled.

During kidney dialysis, the same process occurs artificially. The patient's blood passes through a cellulose tube under pressure, so that the plasma can pass through. Waste products are removed and the plasma is reabsorbed.

Plants

Food (nutrients)

Although green plants and animals both exhibit the same life processes, one fundamental difference is the ability of green plants to manufacture their own food by the process of **photosynthesis**. The predominant colour in the natural world is green due to the chemical called chlorophyll which these plants contain. This chemical compound enables the plant to utilize light energy during the process of photosynthesis, the means by which such plants manufacture food. To do this, plants require carbon dioxide, water, and light as well as chlorophyll. This process of photosynthesis can be summarized in the following way:

carbon dioxide + water $\xrightarrow{\text{light and chlorophyll}}$ sugar + oxygen

A common misconception is that plants get their food from the soil. In fact, they manufacture their own food as shown above, but they do get essential minerals from the soil. However, many plants do not grow in soil at all, for example, floating water plants, some mosses and lichens, and so on. In this case, they obtain their essential minerals from rain, ponds, or even tap water.

Respiration

Plants give out carbon dioxide and take in oxygen. This process goes on all the time. However, in the light they are also photosynthesizing, taking in carbon dioxide to make their food. The result is that during the day the process of photosynthesis dominates, resulting in carbon dioxide being absorbed; during the darkness respiration dominates, and carbon dioxide is given off by plants.

Carbon dioxide and Earth's atmosphere

Plants are the basis of all life, since all animals, including the carnivores, ultimately depend on the ability of plants to manufacture their own food (see above). One major benefit of plant nutrition is the utilization of carbon dioxide, a waste product of respiration in animals and plants and also of many industrial processes. Until recently, the amount of carbon dioxide in the atmosphere was kept fairly constant, as the amount being given off was balanced by that taken up by plants.

In recent years the increased carbon dioxide has resulted in what is known as the 'greenhouse effect'. Carbon dioxide absorbs sunlight and re-emits the infra-red at a very different frequency. The atmosphere is opaque to such radiation, so the energy remains trapped in the atmosphere and earth, thereby causing the average temperature to increase. Scientists predict that this could lead to an overall increase in world temperature, causing the melting of the polar ice caps and the flooding of low-lying areas. They are increasingly appreciating the importance of preserving tracts of open land and forest so that there is a balance between industrial areas and 'green' areas. Although the rainforests may be a long way from Britain, they nevertheless make an important contribution to maintaining the balance of carbon dioxide and oxygen at a global level.

Nutrients are transported in the human body via the blood stream; plants have a similar system, whereby products are transported via the roots, stem and veins to the leaves. The leaves have tiny pores or **stomata** through which gases such as oxygen, carbon dioxide and water vapour can pass.

The life cycle of a flowering plant

Many of the plants which add colour to our gardens each year, such as antirrhinums, asters, lobelias and so on, are referred to as annuals because they complete their life cycle in one growing season. Other plants such as Canterbury bells are biennials: that is, they take two years to complete a life cycle, from seed to producing seeds. Perennials are those plants such as roses which flower each year, the same plant surviving from one season to another.

Plant reproduction

Plants can reproduce both sexually and asexually. In sexual reproduction, a male and a female part from either the same or different plants come together. Pollen is usually then transferred from the stamens, considered to be the 'male' part of the flower, to the stigma, considered to be the 'female' part of the flower, and this results in fertilization of the plant's seeds.

It is possible for parts of a plant other than seeds to grow; for example a potato tuber, a willow twig or a carrot top. In these cases reproduction is asexual (vegetative), as it does not involve the male and female part of the plant.

The parts of a flowering plant

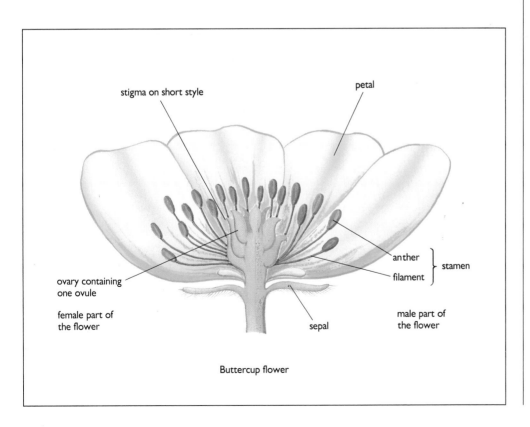

Buttercup flower